Weather

& Crop Protection

Erno Bouma

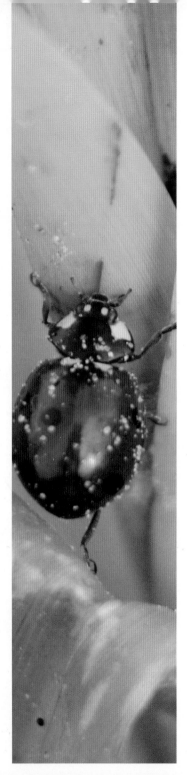

Colophon

Concept
Erno Bouma, Roodbont

Author
Erno Bouma

Editing
Erno Bouma, Marijke van Oostende, Ton van Schie

Translator
Sue Stewart, Stewart Translations

Thanks to
Carel Bouma, Paul Goorden, Lenus Hamster, Hans van Leeuwen, Henk Scheele, Aaldrik Venhuizen, Kees Vogelaar
And to Nick Bradshaw, Leslie Dowley, Mike Krahe, Brian Prince.

Photography
Erno Bouma

Additional photography:
M. van Oostende: p. 6 (Sunrise), p. 25 (Barley), p. 54 (Grass). p. 64 (Computer) - PPO-AGV: p. 9 (Crop) - NFO: p. 9 (Ice-covered branches) - BayerCropScience: p. 12, 49 (Formulation examples) - Plantenziektekundige Dienst: p. 16 (Leafminer) - PPO-AGV: p. 16 (Leek foliage) - PPO-BB: p. 19 (Taxus beetle larva) - Dacom Plant-Service BV: p. 24 (Weather station) - PPO-AGV: p. 26 (Downy mildew) - The Cuticles of Plants (1970): p. 32 (Wax production in peas) - Dacom Plant-Service BV: p. 37 (Phytophthora infection) - PPO-BB: p. 38 (Botrytis in tulips) - PPO-AGV: p. 39 (Rust in cereal foliage) - PPO-AGV: p. 45 (Hail damage in potatoes) - Iiasa Austria: p. 46 (precipitation Europe) - Met Iereann: p. 47 (precipitation Ireland) - Met Office UK: p. 47 (radar precipitation UK) - PPO-BB: p. 48 (Botrytis spores) - Opticrop BV: p. 65 (Temperature and RH sensor) - Dacom Plant-Service BV: p.65 (Phytophthora-infected foliage) - NFO: p. 66 (Scab) - PPO-BB: p. 66 (Botrytis in Lily) - Opticrop BV: p. 68 (Weather pole)

Cover photography
Marcel Bekken (tractor) - www.flip.nl (cloudy sky) - Insets: Marijke van Oostende, NFO

Design and illustrations
Studio Flip, www.flip.nl

Text editing
Maud van der Woude

Roodbont Publishers
PO Box 4103
7200 BC Zutphen, Netherlands
T 00 31 575 54 56 88
F 00 31 575 54 69 90
E info@roodbont.nl
I www.roodbont.nl

Roodbont Publishers is part of Tirion Publishers

Agrometeorologisch adviesbureau Erno Bouma
De Amazone 10
8252 EE Dronten, Netherlands
E bouma.weer@planet.nl
I www.boumaweeradvies.eu

© Roodbont B.V., Agrometeorologisch adviesbureau Erno Bouma, January 2007

ISBN-13 978-90-8740-002-6
NUR 940

Introduction

Why can't you spray insecticides and fungicides together to obtain a good effect? Why shouldn't you tackle volunteer potatoes in a dry, sunny spell? Is it better not to spray at all when there is no wind? Answers to all of these questions can be found in *Weather & Crop Protection*, an essential handbook for arable farmers, contractors, outdoor crop growers and livestock farmers who grow forage crops. In short, for anyone involved in crop protection outdoors.

Bookshelves are already groaning with volumes about the weather, diseases, pests and crop protection, but approaching pest and diseases from the perspective of agrometeorology is something entirely new. Pests and diseases, crop protection and weather are so closely interconnected that it's a wonder nothing like this has been published before.

The central focus of this practical guide is the influence of weather on the effect of crop protection agents. It gives an insight into the role of temperature, humidity, precipitation and wind on pests and diseases and the effect of these weather parameters on the uptake, adhesion and effect of crop protection agents.

Clear descriptions of what happens at plant and leaf level during the uptake and transport of crop protection agents show how best to set about the task of crop protection. Combined with the many practical examples, these descriptions give you a better understanding of the relationship between weather and crop protection. Several widely grown crops with specific product groups receive special attention towards the end of the book, enabling you to identify the ideal weather conditions to maximise the effect of an application.

Weather & Crop Protection is bursting with photos, text boxes, figures and graphs which make the information highly accessible. This unique practical guide is bad news for insects, fungi and other pests, but good news for the farmer!

Contents

1 Sun,
a source of heat

Sunlight provides plants with the radiation they need. Solar radiation affects crop development, the flowering process, and the shape, colour and stem elongation of plants, while temperature has a direct or indirect influence on the application and effect of crop protection products. Unfortunately, the sun is also a source of life for pathogens, fungi and insects.

Solar energy

The sun emits radiation. Some of the radiation that reaches the earth is reflected back. Part of the spectrum is observable as visible light, but there are also invisible regions, i.e. ultraviolet and near-infrared. Much of the radiation emitted by the sun goes unnoticed, such as short-wave gamma radiation and X rays, or long-wave radio and television frequency radiation. This type of radiation becomes noticeable only if there is a sudden, enormous burst of it on the sun. However, much of it is blocked by the atmosphere and never reaches the earth's surface. Radio, television and mobile telephone communications are sometimes severely disrupted during these bursts of hot gases (sunspots). These extremes are of no interest to plants. Crops thrive best on UV-A, blue, red and far-red radiation, from which they derive their growing power. Solar radiation is pure energy.

Global radiation

The radiation falling on a horizontal surface is known as global radiation, which is usually expressed in Joules per square centimetre per day. On a clear, dry summer's day the maximum global radiation in north-west Europe is between 2,800 and 3,100 Joules per cm^2 over the course of a day. On a cloudy day in late December, radiation levels are frequently below 30 Joules per cm^2, only one percent of the level on a sunny summer day!

The amount of radiation is relatively high in the summer. Levels are much lower in southern countries such as Portugal and Italy than in north-west Europe, despite the sun's angle of incidence. This is because summer days are markedly longer in north-west Europe than in the Mediterranean countries. The highest total radiation (an entire day's worth of energy) around the longest day is somewhere in the north of Denmark. Even further north the days are indeed longer in summer, but the sun's angle of incidence is significantly smaller. Even a small country such as the Netherlands experiences differences in day length: the day in the north (North Groningen) is 20 minutes longer than in the south (South Limburg) in the summer (and 20 minutes shorter in the winter).

Low sun

Incoming solar energy is distributed over a horizontal surface. When the sun is lower in the sky, as in winter, the energy is distributed over a larger surface area, which means much less energy per square metre.

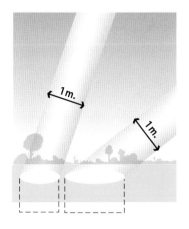

What does the plant see?

A plant 'sees' more than a human being. Even colours outside the visible spectrum are useful to plants. Blue light (400-500 nm) and red light (600-700 nm) have an effect on the plant's photosynthesis. Radiation in this range is known as photosynthetically active radiation, or PAR. Blue light influences crop formation and red stimulates the flowering process. UV radiation (300-400 nm) affects the shape and colour of the plant, while far infrared radiation (700-800 nm) influences stem elongation and flowering.

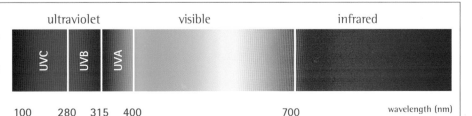

Observable radiation is visible light. Invisible forms include ultraviolet and near-infrared. Both visible and non-visible radiation contain usable energy. Chlorophyll granules absorb mainly blue and red light.

ultraviolet	visible	infrared
UVC UVB UVA		

100   280   315   400   700   wavelength (nm)

Even if the air is not freezing 1.5 metres above the ground, the crop is at risk of freezing.

From Watts to Joules

The intensity of global radiation (the solar radiation falling on a horizontal surface) is expressed in W/m². Adding up the global radiation over a period gives the incoming energy in that period per unit of surface area (power x time = energy). An entire day's worth of energy is the total radiation, expressed in J/cm².

Everything radiates heat

Every object with a temperature above absolute zero (-273°C) emits radiation. The energy emitted increases rapidly as the temperature rises. This radiation is known as heat radiation. In agriculture and horticulture, it is important to know how much energy different types of radiation supply or indeed take away from the soil and crops. The result of this process of give and take is the net radiation. If a crop gains more radiation (= energy) than it loses, it will become warmer. In this case the net radiation is positive.

Night frost

Imagine the crop temperature is precisely 0°C, on a clear, dry, still night. At 0°C the radiation emitted is 316 W/m². Due to water vapour and certain atmospheric gases, the leaves and plants receive only 240 W/m², giving a net radiation figure of -76 W/m². The crop loses more and more energy and cools down. As a result, the air just above the leaves and crop cools down. This means that the air temperature will rise with the distance above the crop. If this situation persists over several hours the crop temperature will fall below freezing point, resulting in a night frost.

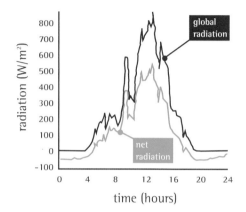

Progression of global radiation and net radiation over the course of a summer's day. Global radiation is zero during the night due to the absence of solar radiation. As a result the net radiation at night is negative, only becoming positive once the global radiation exceeds a certain threshold. It becomes negative again a few hours before the sun goes down.

Conversion table for the different types of radiation

Conversion table for the different energy units in which radiation is represented, using artificial lighting as an example, with the energy output of lightbulbs represented in different units. PAR stands for photosynthetically active radiation.

	Photons (µmol/m²/sec)	PAR (W/m²)	Energy (W/m²)	Light (lux)
Photons (µmol/m²/sec)	1	0.22	0.43	56
PAR (W/m²)	4.6	1	2	260
Energy (W/m²)	2.3	0.5	1	130
Light (lux)	18,000	4,000	8,000	1

Cloud cover: a warm duvet

During a cold night low clouds move in. At ground level, soil and plants cool down the air. Night-time temperatures are lowest at ground level. However, clouds consist of water droplets and water is a good conductor of heat so the temperature of the crop will start to rise. It is not true to say that the clouds will stop the crop from radiating. In fact, it is the other way round: the clouds act as a heater or stove over the plants.

Ice to prevent freezing

Sprinkling is the only way to prevent frost damage. This method works on the principle that heat is released when freezing occurs. This heat ensures that the ovary remains at 0°C: below that temperature fruit tree ovaries will die. As long as water runs over the ice the flower buds will remain at 0°C, even if the air temperature is much lower. If you stop sprinkling the water freezes and the temperature dips below zero, so keep sprinkling until the tem-perature of the ovaries rises above zero again. This stage is reached when the ice falls off. In fruit farming this method uses approximately 3-4 mm of water per hour.

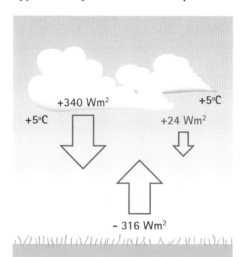

The underside of the cloud layer has a relatively high temperature of around +5°C. The crop radiates −316 W/m^2 at 0°C and receives +340 W/m^2 (because the clouds have a temperature of 5°C). The net radiation goes from strongly negative to +24 W/m^2. The clouds warm up the crop.

In the area of the Netherlands known as the Veenkoloniën or Peat Colonies, mechanical weed control is always hazardous during periods with a risk of night frosts. This operation introduces additional air into the soil and disrupts the conductivity between topsoil and subsoil. Do it in the morning. This will allow the soil to settle over the course of the day and its conductivity to recover to some extent. Carrying out weed control later in the day increases the risk of damage.

Night frost damage

Can a loss of energy be made up by burning oil in halved oil drums? Probably not, because you would have to distribute enormous quantities of energy evenly over the leaves or the crop. The amount of energy that would have to be distributed per hectare is 760 KW/ha. A modern windmill working at full capacity can compensate for the energy loss from just over 2.6 hectares. A medium-sized electricity power station can make up the loss from around 460 hectares. Another option is to hope that cloud cover moves in before it's too late.

Sprinkling can be used to prevent frost damage in fruit trees.

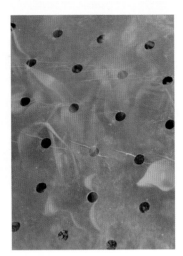

Polythene film retains heat while allowing energy from sunlight to pass through freely.

'Taking the temperature' of a plant's leaves is not straightforward. It calls for special infrared meters with a narrow sensor range. Infrared meters are used in glasshouse horticulture to check the temperature in the glasshouse for example. Their sensor range is too wide for measuring leaf temperatures.

Weather report doesn't tell the whole story

The temperature in weather reports is measured 125 cm above mown grass. However a crop grows on soil. If you look at the temperature progression at different heights (10 cm and 125 cm) on a sunny day, the temperature at ground level is lower in the morning, and higher during the course of the day, than the temperature at 125 cm. Why is this? The sun warms the plants and then the plants warm the air, not the other way round (the net radiation is positive). As a result, the surface of the soil and the crop are warmer than the surrounding air during the day. The leaves of the plants act as a heating element. The difference between the leaf temperature and the temperature at 125 cm may be as much as 10°C. At night the net radiation is negative and the leaves and surface of the soil cool the air down, with the lowest temperatures being found at ground level and close to the leaves.

Warming the soil

To take maximum advantage of sunshine that warms the soil and crop foliage (but not the air) in early spring you can use perforated polytheme film or fleece. The sun's radiation is absorbed by the soil or leaves under the layer of film or fleece. The temperature of the soil and leaves rises, and they then warm the air. These higher temperatures are retained under the film or fleece, advancing the crop.

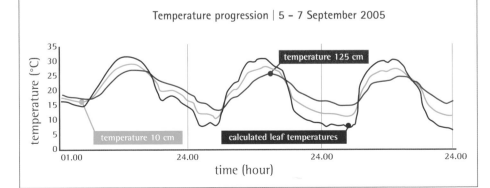

Temperature progression

The daytime air temperature on a sunny day is higher at 10 cm than at 125 cm. The differences between crop temperature and that at a height of 125 cm are often widest during the daytime. At night, the temperature at 10 cm is lower than that at 125 cm. As a rule of thumb, the difference between the air temperatures at 125 cm (red line) and 10 cm above grass (blue line) is as great as the difference between the temperature at 10 cm and the temperature of the leaf itself (purple line).

Temperature progression | 5 – 7 September 2005

Covering beet heaps

In the autumn, harvested sugarbeet are stored in heaps where they are at risk of freezing. The usual advice is to cover the foot of the heap if there is a risk of frost. Only if a harsh frost is expected is it necessary to cover the whole heap. This advice is not always correct.

At night objects radiate energy. The clearer the night, and the colder the surrounding air, the more radiation they emit. Sugarbeets radiate energy too. After a while their temperature falls below zero and they freeze. The beets that were slightly damaged during lifting burn their sugars (reserve food supply) a little faster than normal. This generates a considerable amount of heat, which starts to rise, hence the advice to cover only the foot of the beet heap. However, if a large amount of radiation is emitted and the beets are in the heap for several days, the heat compensation is far from enough to keep the cooling beets at the top of the heap frost-free.

The revised advice is therefore as follows:

- With recently lifted beets, cover the foot of the heap in the event of frost.
- With recently lifted beets, cover the heap completely in the event of frost accompanied by wind.
- If beets have been in the heap for several days already, cover them completely in the event of frost.

Storing starch potatoes

Potatoes are exposed to the same risks as beet in the autumn and early winter. Insulating the heap with plastic and straw, together with the heat generated by the potatoes, is usually enough to prevent frost damage. In the case of potato heaps, also close the ventilation holes in periods of severe frost and wind.

The weather conditions dictate how a beet heap should be covered.

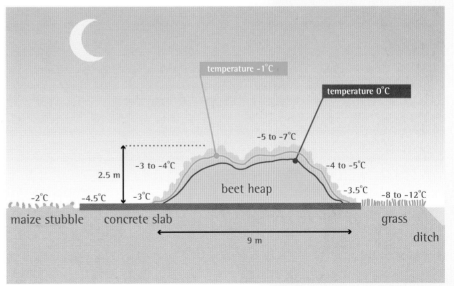

On bright nights harvested beet radiate a lot of energy, as do the grass, the concrete slab and the maize stubble beside the beet heap. The beet, grass and other objects cool down as a result, which is why it is important to cover them correctly. In this case the beet should be covered on top because the temperature there is much lower than the temperature at the base of the heap.

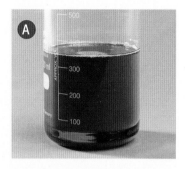

*I*n the case of oil-based formulations the active substance is dissolved in a solvent (a). These liquids are then mixed (emulsified) to produce the spray mixture (b). The spray mixture changes from a clear liquid to an opaque, white, milky liquid (emulsion). It is in this form that the mixture is applied to the leaf cuticle (c).

Effect of temperature

Temperature is seen as vitally important in crop protection, but it is not the only significant factor. Other meteorological factors have a more important effect, such as moisture in the air, leaf wetness duration and precipitation.

Most crop protection products are intended to be absorbed above ground by the leaves or stem. However, leaves and stems are protected by a non-living leaf skin or cuticle. The crop protection product has to penetrate that barrier before it can be absorbed into the living parts of the leaf. It can then be transported, depending on its mode of action. Temperature affects many crop protection products directly:

• By accelerating or improving uptake.
• By accelerating the effect of the product itself.

Formulations

Knowledge of formulations is useful in order to understand how plants absorb products and what factors influence the rate of uptake. Formulating means combining pesticide active substances and auxiliary substances in such a way that the active substance can be distributed effectively. Auxiliary substances include solvents, carriers, emulsifiers and wetting and dispersal agents.

Active substances dissolve in oleaginous or oil-based substances (apolar formulation), or mix with or dissolve in aqueous or water-based compounds (polar formulation). Around 95 percent of formulations are water-based. Take this into account with respect to the desired rate of uptake and also consider the effect of weather factors. For example, contact herbicides such as glyphosate are not absorbed after several days of hot, dry weather.

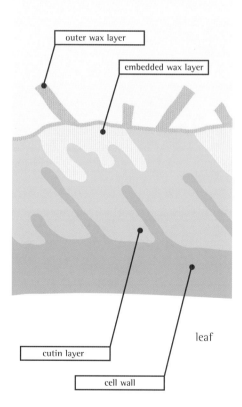

Diagram of a leaf cuticle. The wax layer protects the leaf from drying out, but also makes it difficult for crop protection products to penetrate the leaf.

Rate of uptake

In the case of oil-based formulations, temperature is the only meteorological factor that affects the rate of uptake. Oil-based formulations adhere to the wax layer very quickly. Examples include the emulsifiable concentrates (EC) and oily-flowables (Ofl). All crop protection products with these abbreviations in their trade name or on the label, such as the synthetic pyrethroids (deltamethrin, lambda-cyhalothrin and esfenvalerate), are absorbed very quickly. The higher the temperature (10-15°C), the faster the uptake.

Weakest link dictates rate of uptake

Water-based formulations are also absorbed more quickly when the weather is warmer. These formulations can be identified by the addition of the letters SL, EW, SC or WG to the product name or on the label (eg. Plenum 50 WG or Sencor WG). However relative humidity (RH), soil moisture content and solar radiation are more important than temperature for these formulations. The plant's transpiration rate must be as high as possible for the plant protection products to be transported quickly. If its roots are in soil with a low soil temperature in the spring, the plant's sap circulation will be barely ticking over. The plant may take up the water-based formulations, but it will then transport them very slowly and their effect will be only moderate.

Because plants have their roots in relatively cold soil in the spring, their sap circulation is not at its best. Plants show this by clenching their leaves, reducing their moisture loss. Make sure plants are in top condition before spraying.

Virtually all synthetic pyrethroids are available as oil-based formulations. The solvents in the formulation ensure that the active substance penetrates the wax layer quickly. When sprayed on a dry leaf, the active substance penetrates the wax layer of a tulip leaf, for example, within an hour.

Weather conditions, including the temperature of soil and leaves, play a role in determining how quickly and easily plants can absorb plant protection products.

Persistence and temperature

The active substances in plant protection products such as herbicides and insecticides often work better when the weather is warmer. All of the chemical processes in the plant are speeded up, including specific processes that are targeted by products such as herbicides. Herbicides that inhibit photosynthesis and respiration include phenmedipham, linuron and bentazon. Their effect is enhanced because a greater amount of light (during sunny weather, for example) results in higher temperatures in the leaf and so accelerates the specific processes that are targeted by the herbicides mentioned. If the herbicides have been applied in dull weather, weeds disappear like melting snow when the weather turns bright and warm.
Herbicides from other groups also work better at higher temperatures, such as hormone herbicides (MCPA, mecoprop-P) and modern grass herbicides (such as fluazifop-P-butyl). However, their persistence is shorter. In the case of soil herbicides, a higher soil temperature combined with a good moisture content leads to the faster breakdown of the product by bacteria and fungi in the soil. Higher temperature is good for the effect of an herbicide, but not so good for its long-term persistence.

A soil herbicide such as chlorpropham breaks down quickly in the top few centimetres of warm soil, and also evaporates quickly. In cool, dull weather its effect is prolonged, sometimes by as much as three weeks. A soil thermometer is therefore a useful aid.

Relationship between temperature and required application rate of insecticides

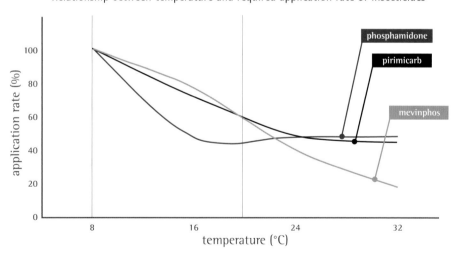

The diagram shows the relationship between temperature and required application rate of the insecticides which correlate positively with temperature, ie. all insecticides with the exception of synthetic pyrethroids. When spraying is carried out in less ideal, cool conditions (8°C) the full application rate is required. At 20°C, however, 60 percent of the full rate is sufficient. The lower application rate does not result in reduced sensitivity (resistance) of the insects to the insecticide.

Insecticides in warm weather

When is the ideal time to spray with insecticide? Insects take on the temperature of their surroundings. An aphid takes on the temperature of the leaf on which it is sitting, a leafminer larva that of the leaf in which it has taken up residence. Their activity increases with temperature. And the more active the insects, the greater the likelihood of them coming into contact with the insecticide. They also exchange more air and eat more. In addition, virtually all insecticides work better at higher temperatures (with the exception of synthetic pyrethroids). But take care! Insecticides break down quickly in strong light conditions. During warm, sunny periods they degrade extremely quickly (sometimes in as little as 12 hours). Always spray in the early evening, when the crop temperature is still fairly high but levels of sunlight can be expected to fall quickly after spraying.

Persistence of cereal fungicides

How long cereal fungicides work against pathogens depends to a large extent on temperature. Fungicides can be subdivided into preventive and curative agents and those with both properties. Temperature dictates how fast fungal mycelium grows in a plant. Some fungi are still capable of killing mycelium tissue in the plant after 20 days if the average leaf temperature has been 10°C. If the average temperature has been 20°C, it is reduced to 10 days. At that temperature, the pathogen spreads through the plant tissue twice as fast.

Insecticides work in three ways:
1. By direct contact.
2. By 'respiration' via the trachea (respiratory orifice).
3. By ingestion via the mouthparts (eating or sucking).
Insecticides usually work via two or three of these routes.

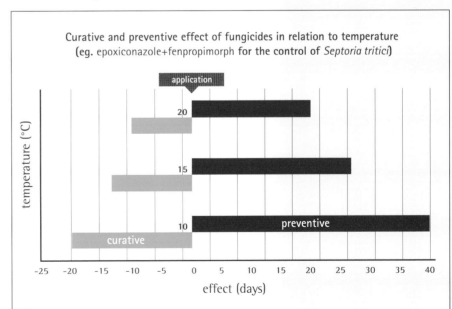

Curative and preventive effect of fungicides in relation to temperature (eg. epoxiconazole+fenpropimorph for the control of *Septoria tritici*)

*P*ersistence of the curative (healing) and preventive (protective) effect of an agent. At low temperatures the curative and preventive effects are long-lasting. If the average daily temperature is doubled, the number of days of preventive effect is halved.

The pea leafminer takes 27 days to develop at 18°C. At 22°C the figure is reduced to 17 days.

Powdery mildew no lover of heat

May and June are the riskiest months for powdery mildew infection in winter wheat for example and severe infection can seriously reduce yield. If the weather in May is dry and sunny, winter wheat will remain largely free of mildew. When the sum is shining brightly on the leaves, leaf temperatures are well above 20°C at that time of year, much higher than the optimum temperature for the pathogen. If the weather is cloudier and more changeable, leaf temperatures tend to be much closer to the optimum temperature of 20°C.

Insects prefer warmth

Insects too have an optimum temperature at which they develop quickest. For example, the rate of development of tobacco thrips is 44 days at 15°C, 15 days at 20°C and 15 days at 30°C. It is the leaf temperatures that are important here, not the air temperatures at 150 cm. This is also one reason why a thrips infestation in leeks on a lighter, sandy soil develops so quickly in early summer sunshine. This is when the leaf temperatures are almost identical to the optimum growth temperature of the thrips.

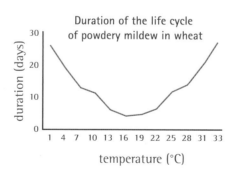

Fungi grow more slowly at temperatures above or below their optimum temperature. This example of powdery mildew in wheat shows that the maximum growth occurs around 20°C (leaf temperature).

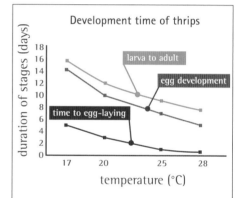

The development time of thrips is strongly temperature-related. In warm, sunny spells thrips damage in leeks is virtually inevitable (see photo).

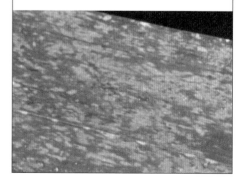

Heat soaks into the soil

Heat spreads in the soil by conduction. Imagine the soil is made up of thin layers. First of all the top layer warms up. Only once the first layer is warmer than the next can heat sink in further. But warming up the first layer takes energy, so less energy is available for the second layer than for the first. Even less energy is left over for the third layer, and so on. The deeper the layer, the less it warms up. In addition, warming the ground takes time. Later in the days the soil starts to cool down again from above. At even greater depths layers are still warming up, albeit not very much.

Risk of bruising

At temperatures below 8°C potato tubers become susceptible to bruising due to knocks and bumps. To reduce the risk of bruising during harvest it is important to know when to check the temperature! First thing in the morning is not a good time. Half an hour after sunrise is the coldest time of the day, above ground at least. It takes a while longer before the coldest time is reached at a depth of 10 cm, is where most potatoes are found. In addition, the time taken depends on the type of soil. On clay soils, it may be a couple of hours. The coldest time of the day is around three hours after sunrise, so wait until coffee time before going out to check the temperature!

Heat penetration

Penetration of temperature at different depths. The deeper the penetration, the less the amplitude (difference between the maximum and minimum temperature) and the later the peak and trough will occur (blue line). A sort of phase shift occurs. The temperature is more stable at greater depth, and hence lags behind, with the delay at a depth of 1 to 2 metres being around two months. If the temperature at the surface fluctuates between -2°C and 25°C, at a depth of 1 metre the corresponding fluctuation is between 7°C and 13°C. This is why deep cellars are cool in summer and warm in winter. The soil too is cold in spring but stays warm in the autumn.

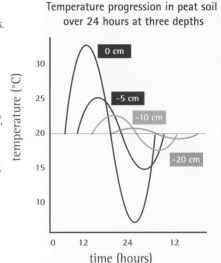

Temperature progression in peat soil over 24 hours at three depths

During warm and sunny weather in June/July, tulips can die back more quickly. This brings the harvest forward by a week or two.

Mulch tulips with straw

At around -4°C tulip bulbs start to freeze. The commonest method used to prevent frost penetration is mulching with straw. This means planting as early as possible and putting a winter mulch on straight away. Soil type and soil structure also influence susceptibility to frost.

In an extended period of hard frosts the ground will freeze even under a straw mulch, but the temperature of the frozen soil layer is not quite as low. Also, the frost penetrates less deeply than it would in the same soil without straw, but thawing is much slower. Frost under straw may stay in the ground longer than it would without a mulch. The straw can be removed around the first of March, provided there is no frost left in the ground at any depth. Note that straw has a temperature-reducing effect above the straw layer in the spring. This increases the risk of night frost damage, which is another reason to remove the mulch before the tulips start to poke through.

Risk of disease

Mulching bulb land does bring a major risk: the risk of disease. Tobacco necrosis as well as Fusarium can infect the bulbs more readily if there are relatively high soil temperatures in the autumn. The critical level is a soil temperature of around 10°C.

Air insulates

Don't loosen the soil too deeply for the seedbed in the spring. An aerated seedbed becomes warmer than a denser subsoil in the daytime, but colder at night. The subsoil under the seedbed stayes colder because it is more difficult for the heat to penetrate downwards. Is there a lot of loose soil after the winter? If so, keep your seedbed preparation to a minimum, as in the case of this frozen soil (photo).

Tulip or other bulbs are best mulched just after planting. Keep the mulch on until the sun gets stronger, around the first of March.

Soil freezes

Soil freezes very slowly. This is because the freezing of moisture in the soil generates a lot of heat which first has to be conducted away. It's no wonder that frost penetration is extremely slow compared with the penetration of a temperature wave. The frost penetration index can be calculated fairly reliably using the frost index and a soil constant. The frost index is the negative total over a 24-hour period of the average surface temperatures from the moment when they become negative.

A lot of insects after a mild winter?

At the end of a mild winter it's often said that there are bound to be a lot of insects in spring and summer. Nothing could be further from the truth. Many insects overwinter in the soil as larvae or pupae. The temperatures at a depth of 2 to 3 cm in the soil rise no higher than -2°C to -4°C during a fairly harsh winter, while temperatures above ground range from -10°C to -14°C. Larvae and pupae are able to tolerate the underground temperatures in a state of winter dormancy.

In mild winters there is often a lot of moisture in the soil. Larvae and pupae in winter dormancy find moisture much more difficult to deal with. Due to the high moisture content and mild temperatures, fungi and bacteria remain active. Fungal tissue attacks and kills many pupae and larvae. This is why hard, dry winters result in a much greater insect burden in spring and summer.

Calculating the frost penetration depth

The frost penetration depth can be calculated using the following formula:

$$\text{frost penetration} = \text{soil type constant} \times \sqrt{\text{frost index}}$$

Soil type	Constant
Dry sand	6
Loam and light clay	4
Heavy clay	3
Peaty soil	2.5
Peat	2

Frost penetration, an example calculation

Day	24-hour surface temperature	Frost index
1	- 4.5°C	4.5
2	- 7.5°C	12
3	1.0°C	11
4	- 5.0°C	16

At the end of the fourth day the frost penetration on sandy building land is $6\sqrt{16}$ cm = 24 cm, compared with 12 cm on heavy clay and 5 cm on grassland on peaty clay.

A lot to do for the ladybird in early spring (the photo shows a ladybird larva). If larvae and eggs of aphids survive the winter.

Insect larvae such as Taxus beetle larvae are not so hard hit by a dry, cold winter. Temperatures in the soil rarely fall below -4°C.

2 Moisture,
something in the air

Moisture in the air plays an important role in many processes in agriculture, such as the release and germination of fungal spores and the wetting of leaves by dew. The extent to which plant protection agents are absorbed by the leaf, or simply run off it, is also largely determined by moisture in the air.

How does water occur in the air?

In nature, water occurs as water vapour and as a liquid at temperatures above zero. At temperatures below 0°C it also occurs as ice. Liquid water occurring at subzero temperatures is termed 'super-cooled'.

Small water droplets don't freeze very easily. In the atmosphere small droplets occur in large numbers in clouds, but they are also found near the ground. The obvious example of this is mist. Water vapour condensing on solid objects is called dew.

Mist forms when the dew point temperature is reached and there are not enough large solid objects in the air to allow all of the moisture to precipitate. This leads to the formation of water droplets, often around particles of dust in the air.

Water vapour in the air

The quantity of water vapour per cubic metre of air is not unlimited. Air that contains the maximum quantity of water vapour it can hold is said to be saturated. One measure of the moisture content of a volume of air is relative humidity, or RH. Humidity is expressed as a percentage of the maximum possible quantity, so saturated air has an RH of 100 percent. The higher the temperature, the more water vapour the air can hold.

Dew point temperature

For agricultural purposes, the dew point temperature is a more suitable way to represent the moisture content of the air. The dew point temperature is the temperature at which the moisture in the air begins to condense on solid objects, such as the leaves of a plant. In general, the dew point temperature remains static over the course of a day unless a different type of air moves in. The RH, on the other hand, fluctuates widely during the course of a day as the temperature rises and falls.

Because one side of the pear is able to emit more radiant energy, the pear is cooler on that side than on the other. As a result, the dew point temperature is reached only on one side, and the pear becomes wet only on that side.

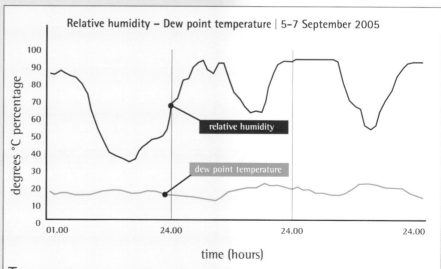

The dew point temperature is a much better measure of the air's moisture content than RH. While RH fluctuates widely over the course of the day, the dew point temperature remains constant. It changes only if a different type of air moves in (moister or indeed drier air).

Human hair also reacts to humidity. When you walk outside from a heated room, your hair grows longer. Not by so much that you would notice it, but the difference is still a couple of millimetres.

Hair hygrometer

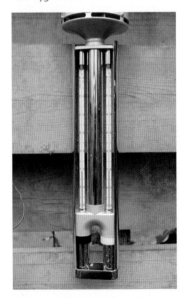

Psychrometer

The psychrometer works on the basis of the dew point principle. The dry thermometer indicates the air temperature. The ventilated wet thermometer evaporates water continuously and indicates the evaporation temperature (= dew point temperature). The RH can be calculated using the following conversion table between the dry and wet bulbs (photo top).

Always hang an RH sensor in a place where its readings are relevant. Suppose you want to measure the humidity in order to decide whether the outside air can be used for ventilation. In this case the sensor should be hung up away from the storage shed, in a small measuring hut called a Stevenson's screen. The sensor should be shielded from direct sunlight.

Measuring humidity

Humidity can be measured most accurately using a properly ventilated wet- and dry-bulb thermometer: a psychrometer. A much simpler measuring instrument is the hair hygrometer. The instrument contains a bundle of hair, usually horsehair. If the humidity rises, the hairs lengthen. If the RH falls, they shorten. These changes in length are conveyed mechanically to a pointer and can then be read off as RH. A hair hygrometer is a cheap and sturdy instrument, but it does require regular maintenance and calibration. Dust particles from the air can easily gather on the hairs in the instrument, especially if it is kept in the potato storage shed for example. The dust particles attract moisture, which affects the accuracy. The solution is to clean such meters regularly. If the meter is in your house, once a year is enough. A meter in the storage shed should be cleaned every two months! The sensors of electronic humidity meters kept in the storage shed to control the automatic ventilation or mechanical cooling tend to accumulate dirt at the same rate. Have sensors of this type calibrated regularly and replace them in good time!

Relationship between **RH**, air temperature and **dew point temperature** (°C)

Air temperature	Relative humidity							
	100%	90%	80%	70%	60%	50%	40%	30%
-10°C	-10	-11	-13	-14	-16	-18	-20	-23
-5°C	-5	-6	-8	-9	-11	-13	-15	-18
0°C	0	-1	-3	-4	-6	-9	-11	-14
5°C	5	4	2	0	-2	-3	-6	-10
10°C	10	8	7	5	2	-1	-4	-7
15°C	15	13	12	10	7	5	2	-2
20°C	20	18	16	14	12	9	6	2
25°C	25	23	21	19	17	14	11	6
30°C	30	28	26	24	21	18	15	10

Some practical examples.

Frozen lily scales

Lily scales with a temperature of 5°C are dried, after rinsing and dipping, using outside air with an air temperature of 5°C and an RH of 60%. When they are almost dry, their temperature is -2°C. They are in the process of freezing!

Condensation

Potatoes in storage sheds have to be ventilated regularly to remove the moisture and heat they produced. Farmers are advised to ventilate using outside air with a dew point temperature two degrees lower than the product temperature, otherwise the potatoes will become wet. If the dew point temperature of the outside air is 5°C and the potatoes are at 7°C, the air passing through the potatoes will always pick up moisture. Had the dew point temperature been 9°C with the same product temperature, the moisture in the air would have started to condense on the relatively cold potatoes.

Drought symptoms

When very high dew points occur in the summer (20°C), growth comes to a virtual standstill because the stomata can no longer exude any moisture to the outside air. There is no transport of moisture from the stomata and the sap circulation grinds to a virtual halt. As a result, pesticides that are intended to be transported via the sap can no longer be expected to have any effect. When low dew points occur, on the other hand, moisture can be lost so quickly that the plant starts to display symptoms of drought and wilt.

In general, fruits do not have any stomata. You should wet or cool strawberries regularly on days with a lot of radiation, because the plant transpires (and cools itself) via the stomata. If this does not happen, damage will occur. This applies to all fruits.

Transpiration

Transpiration requires energy. The stomata of the leaves are constantly trying to shed water during the daytime. The extent to which this happens differs from crop to crop. A bunch of tulips feels much colder than a bunch of chrysanthemums, for example, because tulips transpire more. It takes 2.46 MJ of energy to evaporate 1 kg of water, as much energy as an adult person uses in an hour's gentle cycling. A crop transpiration rate of 1 mm corresponds to 1 litre per m^2. The global radiation on a clear summer's day can occasionally exceed 25 MJ/m^2. If all of the sun's radiant energy were used for transpiration, it would be possible under extreme circumstances to transpire 10 mm of water. Fortunately, transpiration is limited to around five millimetres in extreme situations, because most of the cultivated plants in Western Europe are not capable of transpiring 10 mm per day.

Wind chill

'Wind chill' is a common term in weather reports. The basic principle is as follows: evaporating moisture takes energy. Moisture loss results in cooling. The weather feels colder than it actually is because the moisture on your skin evaporates quickly in a harsh (dry) wind and your skin cools down to below air temperature.

Don't spray if plants are stressed

If plants are suffering from dry conditions, limp or wilted leaves, there is no point in spraying with pesticides that are intended for absorption! They simply won't be absorbed. What is more, substantial damage may occur because the leaves can no longer cool themselves down by transpiration. In such situations leaf temperatures can rise as high as 40°C or even 45°C. If plants are sprayed in such circumstances, there is a greatly increased risk of damage (phytotoxicity).

Transpiration equals cooling

Moist potatoes in a storage shed are dried by ventilating with unsaturated air. No sun is involved; the air itself provides the energy required. Because the air is unsaturated, water evaporates. The energy required is taken from the potatoes. This is also the case in the field. Especially in very windy conditions, when the upper leaves of a crop often transpire much more than leaves deeper down in the crop canopy. The evaporated moisture can be carried away very easily.

The transpiration of a crop can be predicted fairly reliably using Makkink's formula. A fully-grown cereal crop such as barley transpires 4 to 6 mm of water on a sunny day.

Transpiration

Calculating the vital transpiration rate is a complicated business. For most agricultural crops, especially in the growing season, global radiation and prevailing temperature are the most important factors. This makes it possible to use simpler formulae. The simplest is Makkink's formula: $E = G \times A$

E is the transpiration of pasture grass with a good water supply in mm per 24-hour period.
G is the daily total for global radiation in kJ/cm^2.
A is a constant depending on the crop temperature (see table).

The values of A in relation to temperature

Temperature	A-value (mm per kJ/cm^2)
0°C	1.06
5°C	1.27
10°C	1.47
15°C	1.65
20°C	1.82
25°C	1.97
30°C	2.10
35°C	2.22

Heat released from the soil and wind, which is important for carrying away moist air, are not included in the formula. However, this formula is ideal for predicting the transpiration of disease-free grass with a good water supply.

The transpiration during a sunny summer's day is easily calculated: assume the temperature was 20°C and the global radiation 2,500 J/cm^2 (= G in kJ/cm^2). Using the value in the table, the transpiration on that day was 2.5 x 1.82 = 4.6 mm.

*L*arge watery patches surrounded by fungal weft on the green leaves, followed by leaves dying off, is typical of downy mildew in onions. Onion downy mildew is favoured by conditions of high humidity. Crop losses can be significant.

What happens to evaporated moisture?

If we assume the temperature of the air just above a cereal crop is 20°C at an RH of 75 percent, one cubic metre of air contains 12.9 grams of water vapour. The maximum amount of water vapour that a cubic metre of air can hold at 20°C, therefore, is 17.2 grams. There is room for another 4.3 grams per cubic metre of air. That figure is known as the 'saturation deficit'. If a cereal crop was one metre tall, and the air was still down to the top of the crop, only 4.3 grams could evaporate per cubic metre of air. That comes to 0.0043 mm. A fully-grown cereal crop often transpires a thousand times more in the summer, so a thousand times as much air is needed to hold all of the water vapour. In addition, that water vapour has to be carried away (= moisture transport) by the wind.

Moisture transport

Transpiration rate can be a limiting factor for plants. For example, if their roots are not well developed or if they are affected by nematodes or soil-borne fungi such as Pythium and Fusarium, they will be unable to transport sufficient moisture to the stems and leaves. In addition, the soil temperature may still be too low and the roots may not be sufficiently capable of transporting the moisture.

Wind and warmth

First, the wind ensures the mixing of the air in and above the crop. Second, plants make the air not only moister but also warmer. Warmed air can absorb more moisture, and rises, resulting in mixing. Both processes help to ensure that the water vapour released is distributed over a wide layer.

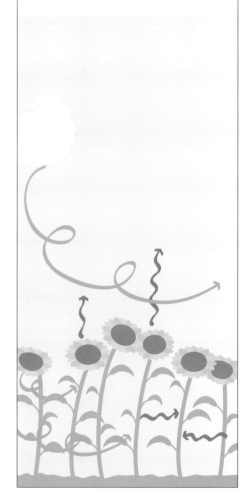

Dew

In the evening, leaves start to cool down and become colder than the air around them. This is because the net radiation of the leaves becomes negative. If this situation persists, their temperature falls below the dew point temperature of the air. The leaves cool down quicker than the air and the leaves become wet as the moisture from the air condenses on them. This process continues throughout the night and stops only when the sun starts to warm the leaves in the morning and the net radiation becomes positive again. The leaves are far from dry at this point, because all of the water that has condensed on them overnight first has to evaporate, which can take several hours. This is known as the leaf wetness duration.

Fungal infections

The leaf wetness duration can play an important role in the germination and infection spores such as Botrytis, yellow rust or *Phytophthora infestans*. It is also important when spraying fungicides. Fungicides do not adhere well to wet leaves and can run off them easily. This period of free moisture also occurs on strawberry or pear fruits, for example.

The amount of dew on the leaves and plants depends to a large extent on the biomass/surface area of the crop. The more biomass there is, the more moisture there is on leaves and stems. The leaf wetness duration is therefore closely connected with the leaf area index of a crop. A heavy crop such as lilies in September or a well-developed potato crop in early August can hold up to 1 mm (or 10,000 litres) of water per hectare.

Leaf wetness duration

The leaf wetness duration depends on the meteorological conditions and the dew point temperature. It increases on average as the season progresses, because the temperature of the soil rises.

Example of leaf wetness duration in a potato crop	
Month	Leaf wetness duration (hours)
April	5.4
May	6.1
June	6.5
July	7.1
August	7.5
September	9.1

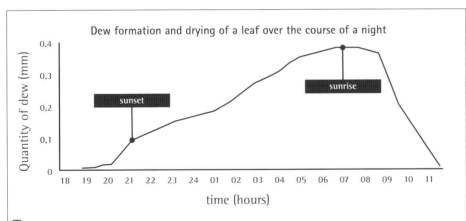

Dew formation and drying of a leaf over the course of a night

The period of leaf wetness can start several hours before sunset. It is shorter and starts earlier on clear days than on cloudy days. There are only a few days each year when this phenomenon does not occur in north-west Europe. These occur mainly in the spring (April/May), in bright, sunny weather with low dew points and a strong easterly wind.

Germination of fungi

For many practical applications, the leaf wetness duration is vitally important. It is also important for the germination of fungal spores and the subsequent plant infection. Spores of foliar fungal pathogens are spread by the wind or via rain splash to land on a leaf. They then have to germinate and dissolve the leaf cuticle with the aid of enzymes. Some pathogens may infect plant leaves via a stoma or other point of entry (e.g. a wound) into the leaf.

In almost all cases this will only succeed if there is sufficient moisture on the leaf surface.

In order to create good conditions for the enzymes attempting to dissolve the leaf cuticle, the cutin layer must be swollen. Is the leaf wetness duration too short? If so, the germ tube searching for a stoma will dry out, as will the germ tube trying to dissolve its way into the leaf. This will succeed only if there is sufficient moisture on the leaf.

It takes several hours of moisture, or a thin film of water on the leaf, to enable spores to germinate and penetrate the cuticle. The germination period is also temperature-dependent. At low temperatures, a fairly long leaf wetness duration is usually required.

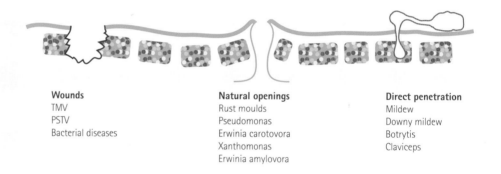

Wounds
TMV
PSTV
Bacterial diseases

Natural openings
Rust moulds
Pseudomonas
Erwinia carotovora
Xanthomonas
Erwinia amylovora

Direct penetration
Mildew
Downy mildew
Botrytis
Claviceps

The graph shows that the leaf temperature fell below the dew point temperature at 7 pm on 6 September. This continued until 7 am on 7 September, a leaf wetness duration of twelve hours.

Temperature 5–7 September 2005

calculated leaf temperature

dew point

Temperature (°C)

Time (hours)

Dew comes from the soil

Moisture from the air condenses on the leaves. This makes the air drier, because condensation removes moisture. A small proportion of the moisture removed from the air is replaced by moisture from the layers of air above the plants. But this is not enough to produce a dewfall of 10,000 litres per hectare. So where does all of that condensed moisture come from? The answer is, from the soil! If the soil is warmer than the air above it, the cold air is able to contain less water and water (dew) will tend to condense at the boundary between warm and cold air.

Water and air

Soil contains water and air, and water evaporates from the soil. Because the air in the soil is generally still, it nearly always has an RH of 100 percent. Soil temperature is not constant at all depths. Moisture is transported slowly by diffusion. As a result, water vapour from the soil can enter the air at the surface. After a clear day the air at ground level becomes colder. The temperature of the soil is higher than that of the air above it. The water vapour in the pores is at a certain pressure. This pressure is higher at high temperatures than at low temperature. The water vapour pressure under the soil is higher than that above it. As a result, the water vapour rises and condenses on the colder crop above.

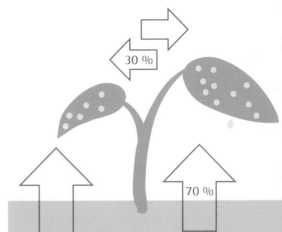

A sort of mini water cycle can be observed between the plants. 70% of the condensed water on the leaves after a wet night evaporates from the soil. The rest (30%) comes from the moisture in the surrounding air.

*T*he adhesion and uptake of crop protection agents also depends to a great extent on whether the leaf cuticle is dry. Crop protection products don't adhere well to a wet cuticle. If it is windy after spraying, or if it rains shortly after spraying, the spray droplets merge with the dew droplets. Then the dew combined with spray droplets runs off the plant. In such situations there is absolutely no point in reducing the spray mixture from 300 to 250 litres per hectare. Remember, the crop can hold up to 10.000 litres of water per hectare!

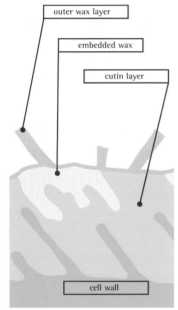

Outside air

outer wax layer

embedded wax

cutin layer

cell wall

The cutin layer in the cuticle swells up and shrinks like a sponge under the influence of moisture. In moist conditions the cutin layer is swollen and plump. In harsh, dry conditions it is very thin. In the latter case the wax layers slide against each other, maximising the leaf's protection against moisture loss. The retention, or the amount of moisture in or on the leaf, is therefore strongly dependent on the development of wax layer and cutin layer.

Uptake of soil herbicides

Most soil herbicides should be absorbed via the roots, but they don't dissolve very easily. Examples include isoproturon and pendimethalin. However, plants use enormous quantities of moisture during transpiration. This process ensures that the concentration of soil herbicides ultimately taken up by weeds becomes high enough to kill them. Basically, the transpiration rate must be as high as possible.

Leaf cuticle: a barrier to absorption?

A plant's leaves are covered on the outside by a skin or 'cuticle'. The cuticle is a vital barrier against the penetration of germinating fungal spores, excessive moisture loss and the absorption of crop protection agents.

The non-living, greasy cuticle is composed of four layers:

1. The outer wax layer.
2. Embedded wax.
3. A cutin layer.
4. The cell wall.

Potatoes have a very thin wax layer and hence high retention. As a result, systemic or translaminar fungicides are easily absorbed.

A thick outer wax layer limits transpiration. This is particularly evident in crops from dry, warm areas with very low retention.

Wheat has a much better-developed wax layer than potatoes, and much lower retention. In arid conditions this may inhibit the uptake of foliar fertilisers and systemic pesticides. The grey layers on the leaves are wax layers.

Onions have a very well-developed wax layer and low retention. This, and the shape of the leaf, often makes an onion leaf difficult to wet.

Selectivity

Whether or not the leaf cuticle lets certain substances through is known as selectivity. The permeability of the cuticle depends on its structure, which is proportionately much thicker – sometimes up to a thousand times thicker – than the wall structure of the other cells of the plant. There may also be variation in selectivity between plants: old leaves have a thicker wax layer and hence a thicker cuticle, than younger leaves.

Old or young leaves

Older grass leaves have a more horizontal leaf position. In addition, plants such as annual meadow grass, ryegrasses and volunteer cereals absorb pesticides more easily through the older leaves. For the control of grass-like weeds, the vegetative development should therefore be more advanced as there also has to be sufficient older foliage to absorb the herbicide. Dicotyledons, on the other hand, absorb agents most easily via their youngest leaves, so apply herbicides early against dicotyledons such as redshank, fat hen, chickweed and mayweeds.

Control chamomile when the plant is still very young. Product uptake will be much better than in a slightly older specimen such as the one in the photo.

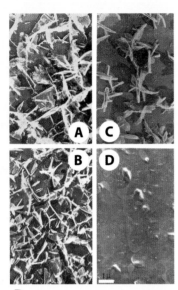

*P*ea leaves grown under different light intensities. Leaves produce larger numbers of wax structures in good light conditions than they do under darker conditions.

A good light (406 lux)
B 65% less light (140 lux)
C 80% less light (84 lux)
D no light

Dynamics of the wax layer

In dry weather, with a low relative humidity, high radiation and dry soils (which is very important), a plant produces more leaf wax than normal. As the plant risks transpiring more water than it can afford to lose, this increases its protection against drying out: this is known as hardening off. It is not only the thickness of the wax layer that changes under these conditions, so does its structure. This has a substantial effect on the uptake of most pesticides.

Wax inhibits absorption

Most pesticides are sprayed in water. The 250 to 500 litres of water per hectare are turned under pressure into small droplets (100 μm- 250 μm) which fall on the leaf. If the leaf has a thick wax layer the droplets will remain on top of that layer. The surface tension of the droplets is too great. Surface-active substances, which are added to many formulations, may provide the solution.

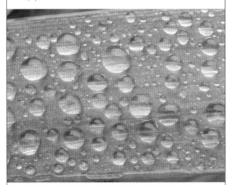

Effective absorption is out of the question here.

*T*he droplet on the right is perched on top of the wax layer. A surface-active substance has been added to the droplet on the left. The difference in retention (adhesion of moisture to the cuticle) is clear.

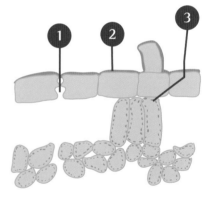

*C*ross-section of a leaf. Crop protection products are absorbed by (2) and through (3) the cuticle. Stomata (1) are only capable of gas exchange. The myth that crop protection products dissolved in water are able to penetrate via the stomata is just that: a myth.

How are products absorbed?

Many people believe that pesticides are absorbed mainly via the stomata, but this is not correct. The spray droplets are invariably too large to enter a leaf through the stomata. Even if the droplets sprayed on to the leaf merge together to form a film, the surface tension of the spray mixture is still too high to allow it to penetrate via the stomata.

In practice, pesticides can be absorbed by the stomata if they are in vapour form. This is only relevant if they have to act in that way in order to be effective.

Monocotyledonous plants do not absorb crop protection products well at an early stage. It makes sense to wait a while.

Dicotyledonous plants do not absorb crop protection products well later on, so spray as soon as possible! In the photo the short stem is redshank, with chickweed at the bottom.

Oil-based formulations are absorbed via the embedded wax. This is a relatively quick process: they penetrate the embedded wax in less than an hour. The solvents in the formulation dissolve the wax layer and the active substance in solution quickly penetrates. Then the spray mixture and solvent evaporate. All other formulations, i.e. water-based formulations, have to be absorbed via the cutin layer of the leaf. This is possible only if that layer is swollen and plump, i.e. under moist conditions with adequate retention.

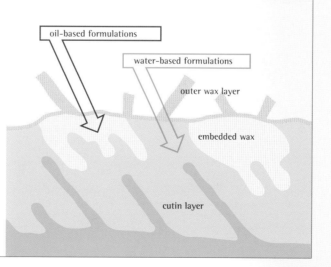

oil-based formulations

water-based formulations

outer wax layer

embedded wax

cutin layer

Oil-based formulations

Oil-based formulations are intended to enter the plant's moisture circulation system by diffusion from the wax layer. A key indicator that says something about how systemic crop protection products are is how well they mix with water. If they have low miscibility, they remain in the wax layer after absorption. If they have high miscibility, they are absorbed into the sap circulation. Temperature is an important factor as it determines the speed of absorption by the wax layer. Synthetic pyrethroids (such as delta-methrin, lambda-cyhalothrin and esfenvalerate) are not easily transported by the moisture within the plant, so are not systemic. Glyphosate and dicamba, on the other hand, are transported very easily.

Water-based formulations

In the case of water-based formulations, many more meteorological conditions are important. Polar substances are intended to be absorbed via the cutin layer by diffusion. That layer must first be very swollen with moisture that was already on the leaf. The relatively small quantity of spray mixture is not enough to swell the cutin layer. On average, transport through the cutin layer takes around six hours with formulations of this type. If the spray mixture dries up soon after spraying, due to very drying conditions and bright sunshine for example, this does not necessarily always spell doom for the spraying outcome. High light intensities, high temperature, strong wind and low RH acceler-

ate the evaporation of the water (acting as solvent and carrier) and shorten the potential absorption time. As a result, less of the active substance is able to penetrate.

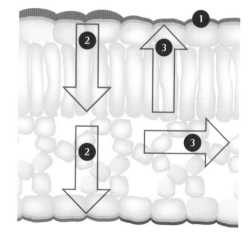

*P*esticides have different final destinations after spraying. Contact pesticides need only be applied to the leaf and adhere properly (1). Translaminar products diffuse through the leaf and also work on the other side of the leaf (2). Systemic products are transported via the leaf by the vascular tissue to the tips of leaves or stems (3). Local systemic products work over a slightly larger surface area (compared with the area of the spray droplet).

The right time to apply

In dull, good growing weather with some precipitation, an arable farmer gets his spraying equipment ready. After a few days like this, conditions are best for virtually all pesticide applications intended for absorption i.e. herbicides that work via the leaf, hormone herbicides, systemic insecticides and fungicides and foliar applied fertilisers. Their absorption and effectiveness are so much better that it nearly always pays off to wait for these ideal conditions.

Identifying the right time to apply water-based contact herbicides such as MCPA and glyphosate is a matter of precision. The plants' cutin layer must be as swollen as possible, which is usually the case after a few days of dull, rainy, good growing weather. During application and for 48 hours afterwards the RH must be high, and there shouldn't be too much radiation.

Good growing weather

Warm, dry and sunny weather is a lot more enjoyable, of course, but don't expect a pesticide to have its maximum effect in such conditions, because the plants won't be able to absorb it sufficiently. Examples of agents to which this applies include all hormone herbicides, glyphosate, metribuzin (at low application rates), and bentazone. Apply these only in good growing weather! If the application conditions are ideal you can often cut back a bit on the application rate.

Good growing weather.

Warm and sunny weather.

Control of volunteer potatoes

In dry, hot weather there is no point in controlling volunteer potatoes with glyphosate. Sprayed potato leaves drop off because the salt concentration soon becomes excessive as water quickly evaporates from the glyphosate solution. The leaf becomes scorched and the plant absorbs hardly anything. It is better to control volunteer potatoes in good growing weather, when the soil contains plenty of moisture, radiation levels are moderate and the RH is fairly high.

Identifying the ideal time for weed control using a water-based herbicide is a matter of precision.

Water containing the pesticide in solution or mixture form has to be absorbed into the leaf. Often, absorption extends no further (wider) than the surface on which the droplet lies. If you increase the surface area of the droplet, the absorption process will be better and faster. For example, an onion leaf is narrow and very waxy. If you spray this leaf you won't obtain total coverage. With the aid of a spreading agent, a larger area of the leaf can be protected. The photo on the left shows droplets on an onion leaf without spreading agent. The photo on the right is the same treatment with the addition of a spreading agent. The result is much better coverage (retention).

Adjuvants

For adhesion and distribution over the leaf surface (i.e. the cuticle), a thin film of spray mixture over the entire surface is ideal. The size of the spray droplet and the solvent are vitally important in this respect. Adjuvants, such as spreading/wetting products, are often added to the formulation. These substances lower the surface tension of water, improving adhesion and spread. The result is better retention or more moisture, containing pesticide, on the leaf. Spreading agents are saponaceous (soap-like) compounds which have a polar (lipid-repelling) and an apolar (lipid-attracting) part. This enables them to create a link between water and wax layer, resulting in better wetting (spreading agents include Frigate). Other adjuvants can be used to improve penetration of the leaf (such as Agral).

Ideal formulation

The agrochemical industry strives to create the best possible pesticide formulations and devotes a great deal of attention to finding the ideal formulation. The liquid or powder often contains surface-active substances already. Don't experiment with adding extra surface-active substances yourself; seek advice from your agronomist, advisor or consultant.

Release of fungal spores

Relative humidity (RH) often plays a role in the process of spore production and dissemination. If the RH falls over the course of the day as the temperature rises, the number of spores of e.g. *Phytophthora infestans* in the air increases enormously. The spores of many fungal pathogens are borne on specialised fungal strands (mycelium) usually on stalks that arise perpendicular to the tissue. In late blight of potato (*Phytophthora infestans*), there is one branched stalk called a sporangiophore and this is a single cell on which

the Phytophthora spore (sporangium) sits. This cell reacts to RH. If the RH falls, the sporangiophore twists and soon after the Phytophthora spore snaps off. This can be seen if a potato leaf with a severe Phytophthora infection is studied under a binocular microscope. Due to the heat of the light source of the microscope - and the resulting lowering of the RH - the sporangiophores start to twist. The largest wave of Phytophthora spores passes through the countryside early in the morning, when the RH is at its lowest. This information is incorporated into some late blight decision support systems.

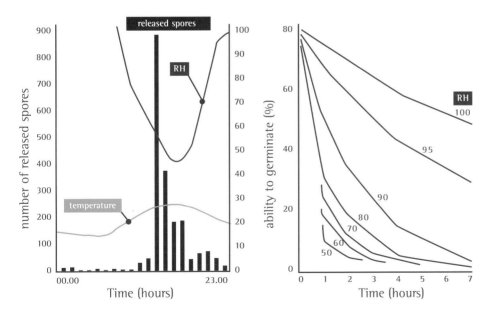

The release of Phytophthora infestans sporangia. After spreading, sporangia still have to germinate before they can pose a risk. Their ability to germinate is closely associated with RH. If the RH is high over an extended period, their germination ability is also high. If the RH is low, their germination ability falls sharply because the sporangia desiccate.

Phytophthora infection.

*B*otrytis can destroy large quantities of green growth in a short space of time, for example in Gladiolus as these trial plots show. The resulting infection had an adverse effect on the yield in kg and bulb size. Good protection makes good sense.

Leaf wetness and fungal infection

Many fungi, such as powdery mildews, downy mildews, *Botrytis* spp and *Phytophthora infestans*, need a certain period of leaf wetness in order to germinate and infect the leaf. Leaf wetness duration is associated with temperature. A Botrytis (fire) infection in tulips, for example, needs a leaf wetness duration of 72 hours at a temperature of 5°C. At 20°C it needs only 24 hours to establish a successful infection.

Just before and during germination, the spore is extremely vulnerable. Sometimes, the spore has already germinated but the leaf is not yet infected. If the conditions then turn unfavourable (i.e. dry and sunny), the germinated spore will die. What if the spore's germ tube has already penetrated the leaf cuticle and reached the underlying tissue? In this case, only the leaf temperature will determine how fast the pathogen grows.

Botrytis infection rate in tulips, depending on temperature and leaf wetness duration

Leaf wetness duration (hours)	Temperature (°C)			
	5	10	15	20
6		0	0	0	0
24	0	6	26	100
48	11	65	70	100
72	100	100	100	100

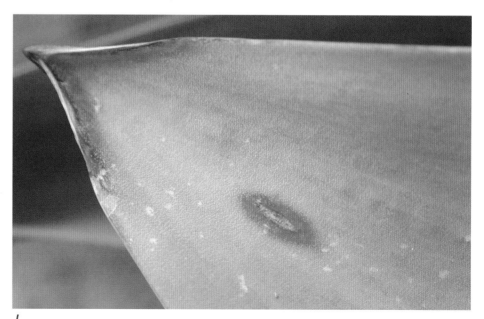

*I*nvestigations were carried out to establish the leaf wetness duration required at a given temperature in order for fire pathogen (Botrytis) to germinate in and infect tulips. The information obtained is used in decision support systems.

When to apply contact fungicides?

Contact fungicides or preventive fungicides, such as mancozeb, fluazinam or captan, are intended to work on the outside of the plant to prevent fungal spores from germinating or penetrating. Apply these at a time when the plants are dry, to maximise their adhesion. The weather conditions after application should also be drying.

The ideal time is in the afternoon, in clear, sunny weather with a slight breeze. The drying time under such conditions is around an hour. Never apply a contact fungicide early in the morning when a crop is wet with dew. The crop will contain a large amount of water from the dew.

Systemic fungicides

Systemic fungicides, such as the cereal fungicides tebuconazole and epoxyconazole, are intended to be absorbed by the cutin layer. To ensure that this layer is sufficiently swollen, you need to wait for good growing weather. Apply the agent preferably in the early evening, during a dull period and in a dry crop. Or in the morning in a crop that is almost dry, in a spell of dull weather. Systemic fungicides should also not be sprayed on a crop that is wet with rain or dew!

The strobilurins, such as trifloxystrobin and kresoxim-methyl, are a bit of a mixture. They have a local systemic effect, a contact effect and a vapour effect. Within the strobilurins group, moreover, there are substantial differences between these three modes of activity.

Always spray a contact fungicide for the control of Phytophthora in potatoes or Botrytis in bulbs at a dry time of day, e.g. in the afternoon.

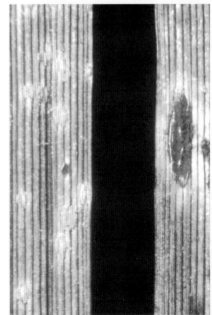

Products for the control of Septoria (left) and rust (right) in cereal crops are best sprayed in the early evening or in the morning on a drying cereal crop.

Transport of products in the plant

Leaf temperatures can soar due to radiation from the sun. The leaves may respond by transpiring water via the stomata. Transpiration takes heat (= energy) from the leaf, causing it to cool down slightly. The RH must be lower than 100 percent, otherwise the stomata cannot exude the water vapour. Under these conditions, the plant's sap circulation also continues to function, which is important for the transport of systemic agents for example. Such agents have to be carried along with the sap in the vascular tissue. The vascular tissue transports fungicides and insecticides throughout the plant to all of its extremities: the stems and leaves. In the case of some herbicides, transport via the sieve tubes can take them even further, to the underground parts.

Downy and powdery mildew

Diseases that block (downy mildew) of destroy plant cells (powdery mildew) have a typical temperature effect. The destruction of cell membranes releases additional moisture. In cucumber leaves this results in a temperature decrease of 0.8°C. There is then a deficit of transport of moisture. Cooling no longer works and the temperature rises again.

Blockage and attack can disrupt the transport from vascular tissue to the cells to such an extent that crop protection products can no longer reach their target – the fungal, so always apply systemic, curative products at an early stage of development of the fungal.

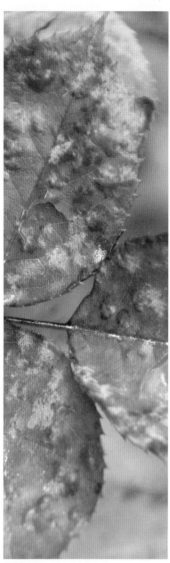

This rose leaf is severely affected by mildew. The sap circulation is disrupted to such an extent that a proper through-flow of curative fungicides is no longer possible. There is no longer any point in spraying.

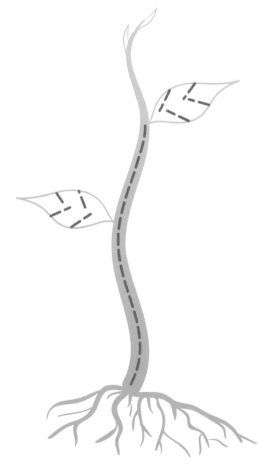

Spraying with a cereal fungicide does not necessarily protect the whole plant. Fungicides with a systemic effect work on the outgrowth only. They are transported to the extremities of the leaves, not to the growing points.

Drying equals cooling

Potatoes, onions and flower bulbs have to be ventilated with outside air to dry them when storing in sheds. After that the farmer's main objective is to bring their temperature down and then to keep it as constant as possible. Moisture produced by transpiration of the tubers must also be removed, together with the heat generated by the stored products.

The ventilation air must be drying. A guiding principle in this respect is the dew point temperature, or the temperature at which the moisture in the air starts to condense. If the dew point temperature is higher than the temperature of the stored product, the moisture from the ventilation air will condense on the product and everything will become soaking wet, so make sure the dew point temperature is two degrees lower than the product temperature during ventilation.

Potato and onion storage

Here are two examples of good moisture removal (situations A and B) and an example where moisture removal is more difficult (situation C). See also page 23.

Situation A. *The potatoes in a storage shed have a temperature of 8°C, the outside air is at 8°C and the dew point temperature of the outside air is 5°C. This air is ideal for ventilation purposes because there is no risk of the moisture from the outside air condensing on the potato tubers. The moisture in the shed is easily removed and the temperature of the potatoes does not go up.*

Situation B. *The onions in a storage shed have a temperature of 1°C, the outside air is at 5°C and the dew point temperature of the outside air is -2°C. This air is ideal for ventilating because the moisture from the outside air will not start to condense on the onions.*

Situation C. *The potatoes in a storage shed have a temperature of 8°C, the outside air is at 2°C and the dew point temperature of the outside air is -5°C. It is difficult to ventilate using this air. It can be done, but only at very low fan air speeds. In this case it is better to ventilate using combined air: the air that is already inside and a small proportion of air from outside. This is because the outside air is very dry.*

3 Precipitation,
a gift from the gods

Water falls to earth as rain, hail or snow. It soaks
into the soil, is taken up by plants or flows away over
and through the soil. Ultimately, it evaporates again
to become water vapour in the air, completing the water cycle.

Aim of application

Anyone who is spraying or has just
sprayed a pesticide will be familiar with
this question: the spraying was carried
out under good conditions, but it rained
shortly afterwards. Is this a problem? That
depends to a large extent on the type of
spray. First, you need to know how the
agent is formulated. If it is an oil-based
formulation (EC or Of), it is usually not
too bad if it rains soon after application.
With virtually all other formulations,
however, it is a problem. Second, the reason why you are using the agent is important, as is the type of agent, e.g. is it a
soil-acting herbicide or a contact-acting
herbicide? In the latter case, rain soon
after spraying means that virtually the
whole lot will be washed off again.

Where does rain come from?

Warm air rises, together with the moisture that it contains. The temperature of the air falls as it rises, by approximately 1°C per 100 metres on average. The RH of the cooling air increases until the point when the air becomes saturated. The moisture begins to condense into tiny droplets around the myriad dust particles in the air, forming a cloud. If the air rises even further the droplets become supercooled (-10°C to -15°C) and freeze, forming ice crystals. These clump together to form snowflakes. If those snowflakes are large and heavy enough, they start to fall. The moist air in this shower has now risen to an altitude of around 6-8 km. On their way down the snowflakes melt and fall to earth as raindrops.

A rain cloud consists of fine water droplets. But if this cloud is to produce rain, the droplets first have to freeze, cluster together and fall as snowflakes. All of the precipitation in Western Europe, in both summer and winter, falls to earth as snow.

If a well-developed cloud is shaped like an anvil at the top, the top of the cloud is icy. This is often a sign that it is starting to rain under the cloud. If you see this, you should certainly postpone any spraying.

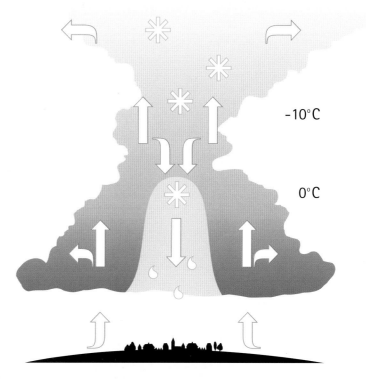

-10°C

0°C

In the summer months the air in storm clouds can rise to an altitude of 13-14 km. The average storm cloud quickly grows to 30 km. Clouds like these contain very strong air flows. On their way down, snowflakes/raindrops can pick up a lot of speed and merge to form large droplets.

*D*ue to splashes of soil on leaves, eyespot disease in cereals and Botrytis in strawberries or tulips can sometimes spread from the soil to the leaves or stems. Diseases also spread from foliage to foliage, e.g. in the case of Septoria tritici or leaf blotch in wheat.

The force of raindrops

The force of a raindrop depends on its kinetic energy and the impact duration. The larger the raindrop, the greater its mass. Raindrops range in diameter from less than 0.1 mm in the case of drizzle to 5 mm in the case of torrential rain. A 4 mm raindrop falls with a speed of around 6 m/s and a 1 mm raindrop at 3 m/s. The mass of the 4 mm raindrop, however, is 64 times greater than that of the small drop. The energy released on impact is 256 times as great (see box). And that is when there is no wind. If it is very windy, the speed is even greater. Impacts can cause all sorts of damage. For example, some of the wax layer of the plant can be washed off and grains of sand can damage the cuticle. As a result, early protection against Botrytis is desirable. Or particles of soil containing fungal spores or bacterial slime can be splashed up. The impact force also depends on the impact duration and the distortion of the raindrop.

> ### For the maths buffs among us
> The impact energy can be calculated using the formula $E(k) = \frac{1}{2}mv^2$. The energy released by a large raindrop on impact is $\frac{1}{2} \times 64 \times 6^2 = 1.152$ Nm.
> The corresponding figure for the small raindrop is $\frac{1}{2} \times 1 \times 3^2 = 4.5$ Nm. The large raindrop therefore releases $1.152/4.5 = 256$ times as much energy.

*P*lastic or glass rain gauges are normally used in agriculture. However, these do not collect enough water. A good rain gauge has a collection aperture of 200 cm² and a design that virtually eliminates evaporation.

*R*eliable electronic precipitation meters have also been developed in recent years. These work on the tipping bucket principle and emit a pulse that can be recorded electronically.

Hailstones: like a yo-yo

Hailstones falling to earth in a heavy shower are merely raindrops that have been carried up and down repeatedly, like a yo-yo, to an altitude of 8 to 10 km. The layer of moisture around each hailstone has frozen again each time. This demonstrates the sort of forces at work in a hail cloud: balls of ice 0.5 to 1 cm in diameter are propelled upwards over and over again to an altitude of 8 km!

Hail damage

Hailstones fall at the same speed as raindrops of the same size, and they have the same mass. However, their impact force is much greater. This is because a raindrop distorts greatly on impact, and a hailstone does not. The impact duration of a hailstone is much shorter and its force proportionately greater. As a result, hailstones can damage the leaves of plants very quickly. They can even punch holes in them.

Hail damage in potatoes.

Can a river hold back a storm cloud?

The idea that a storm cloud can be stopped in its tracks by a canal or river is absolute nonsense. A storm with a surface area of 30 km^2 and clouds at an altitude of 9 to 13 km takes little notice of things on the ground. The storm is driven by the prevailing wind direction at that altitude. A storm cloud does suck in a lot of air, though, which may make it look as if it is advancing into the wind.

*R*ain and hail usually fall from a storm cloud in bands, so check crops carefully for damage. Damage is not usually visible from the roadside.

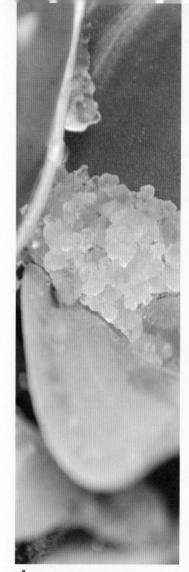

A hailstone is formed in several stages. If you cut one in half, you can see concentric rings. The number of rings indicates how many times the hailstone was carried upwards in the storm cloud.

Europe annual precipitation

Distribution of annual precipitation over Europe. The light (yellow) areas are relatively dry (ca. 500 mm per year). Blue = 800 - 900 mm per year, violet = over 1600 mm per year.

Precipitation pattern in Europe

Some places in Europe are wet, some are not so wet. This may be due to differences in altitude: eastern and southern parts of Germany are markedly drier. This is partly because these areas lie in the shadow of mountain ranges, and partly because the distance from the ocean is much less. If we look at the wettest places in north-western Europe, the mountainous areas stand out. Scotland, Wales, Switzerland and Austria are by far the wettest areas in Europe. Ireland too is a contender, with its high precipitation levels. The prevailing wind direction in north-western Europe is west-southwesterly. It can be cautiously concluded from the pattern of precipitation that the Netherlands and Belgium are in the rain shadow of the United Kingdom to some extent.

Wide differences from year to year

On average, around 800-850 mm of precipitation falls in north-western Europe each year. There are wide differences from year to year and between the seasons, which is a vital piece of information for the agricultural sector. In the summer in particular, the difference in shower

In Wageningen and De Bilt, measurements are being carried out to determine the duration of precipitation. The findings show that it is dry around 92 percent of the time in the Netherlands. That means it almost never rains in the Netherlands!

The Netherlands is actually too small to display differences in precipitation intensity. Taking a slightly broader view, it is immediately clear that in Central and Eastern Germany for example the number of sprayings to control potato blight is significantly lower than in the Netherlands (50 to 70 percent of the Dutch figure). The Germans therefore have the advantage of fewer hours of rain and fewer hours of leaf wetness. These differences are also found in the United Kingdom, where the west of England, Wales and Scotland is much wetter than the east.

Difference in rainfall between two neighbouring farms after a showery day. The rain gauges were 400 metres apart.

situations with little wind over several kilometres can sometimes be as much as 100 mm, which is slightly over a month's worth of precipitation on average. To put it even more strongly, the differences in precipitation levels during showers can be as much as 20 percent or more at short distances (25 metres).

Precipitation forecast

Possible ingredients for a precipitation forecast include type of precipitation, period, intensity and total precipitation. Any forecast involves an element of uncertainty. Sometimes it makes sense to include that uncertainty in the forecast, but using such uncertainty does require a certain level of understanding.

Suppose a precipitation forecast predicts a 40 percent chance of precipitation in the day and showery weather is expected with 10 mm of precipitation at national level. It is impossible to say when the rain will start and stop. Where it rains, you have to expect an average of $100/40 \times 10$ mm = 25 mm.

Usefulness of rainfall radar

The use of ordinary or specialised rainfall radar images is more the rule than the exception nowadays. Rainfall radar can show a number of things:
- A band of precipitation in the case of a front.
- An absence of precipitation.
- A shower pattern.

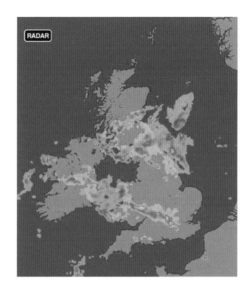

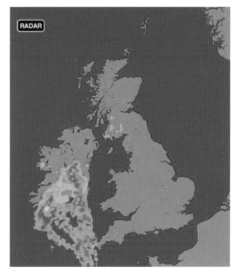

Looking at several images in succession gives you an idea of where the precipitation is heading, and how fast. You can take this into account when planning your spraying schedule. Don't forget to take account of the pesticide's drying time.

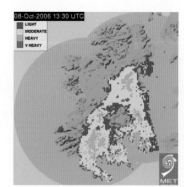

Radar shows where precipitation is occurring, but the latest image is at least 5-15 minutes old. From a meteorological perspective, the scattered distribution of the showers/precipitation indicates that the air type is likely to lead to the formation of showers. When you study a rainfall radar image, many places may be free of precipitation. But when you come to spray, that cloud right over your head may decide to rain on you. In a situation like the one on this radar image, think about putting your spraying off for a while!

Water condensation on a joint.

Sprinkle irrigation and crop protection

Sprinkle irrigation influences plant diseases and the effectiveness of crop protection agents. If it is necessary to irrigate due to a moisture deficit at root depth and the leaves remain wet for long periods, always irrigate during the day. Otherwise the leaf wetness duration is artificially extended and this will encourage disease caused by fungal pathogens. Irrigation does however wash off some of the wax layer as well as any preventive contact fungicides used.

This is why for a disease such as potato blight you should try to restore plants' protection with repeated fungicide treatments as soon as possible after irrigating. Chosing the right spray window can be important here. On soils that dry quickly, spraying can take place after irrigating. On soils that can't be travelled so quickly, spraying should take place up to six hours before irrigation, provided there is reasonable drying weather. Some of the pesticide will wash off immediately during irrigation, but the remainder will still afford sufficient protection. Adjust and reduce the spraying interval if necessary.

Not too cold

People with practical experience say that the temperature of the irrigation water should not be too low since this would cause the crop a lot of damage. They note that the aluminium joints of the sprinkle irrigation system become wet with condensation during irrigation. But the temperature of spring water rarely falls below 10°C, which is certainly not too cold. The joints become wet because the dew point temperature of the air is above 10°C, so the moisture from the air condenses on the joints. The temperature of 'ordinary' raindrops is almost always lower than this; they are melted snowflakes after all.

Leaf damage due to sprinkle irrigation is hardly ever due to the temperature of the irrigation water. The salt or iron content of the water is usually the culprit.

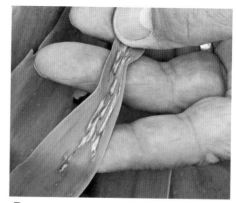

Botrytis spores can be splashed from leaf to leaf and a disease like tulip fire can spread rapidly in showery periods.

Precipitation after spraying

The possibility of a crop pesticide being washed off by rainfall after spraying is an ever-present risk. The effect of precipitation depends on the formulation. The main spray agents in powder form are water-soluble powders (SP), spray powders (WP or DF) and spray granules (WG). All of these are water-based formulations. Formulations in powder form are dissolved in the water in the spray tank, or they are present in the water as a suspension (floating in very small particles) and are sprayed in that state. Water is therefore used as a carrier and sometimes as a solvent. Water-based formulations have to be applied to dry plants in order to adhere properly to leaves or stems. Adhesion is still difficult because a wax layer is greasy and so water-repellent. In addition, it is particularly important with this type of formulation that the weather should remain dry for several hours after application.

Liquid formulations

Well-known liquid formulations are emulsifiable concentrates (EC), emulsions (EW), aqueous solutions (SL) and suspension concentrates/flowables (SC). Emulsifiable concentrates are oil-based formulations where the active substance is dissolved in oil-based solvents. The application of ECs is relatively independent of the weather. They soon become rainproof because they dissolve quickly in the wax layer. However, a drawback is the fact that they make the plant slightly more susceptible to

frost. There is also a greater risk of damage because symptoms of scorching (phytotoxicity) can occur more rapidly. The reason why plants become more susceptible is not well understood.

Other liquid formulations, like formulations in powder form, have to be applied to a dry leaf. And the leaf must remain dry for several hours after application.

Leaf damage in caraway: the leaf has been partially scorched by an excessive concentration of crop protection agent.

The label tells you which type of formulation you are dealing with.

These granules dissolve clearly in the water. The advantage of granules is that less product blows away during preparation of the formulation.

Apply soil-acting herbicides on a moist soil to maximise the effect of their distribution and absorption on germinating weeds.

Herbicides

In the case of herbicides, it is important to distinguish between weather conditions that are important in the application of soil-acting herbicides and contact-acting herbicides, e.g. whether the leaf is wet. It is also important to distinguish weather conditions that are important in terms of the effect, for example if the soil contains sufficient moisture, and the radiation level.

Most soil-acting herbicides need a short spell of dry weather, and moist soil, after application. The herbicide must be able to dissolve in the soil moisture and be able to spread horizontally by diffusion. Then moisture is needed to enable the herbicide to soak deeper into the soil. In the case of soil-acting herbicides (including metazachlor) absorption by the roots is the main route: they dissolve in water and are conveyed to the roots of the plant.

Contact-acting herbicides are absorbed by the stems and leaves of the plant. Their susceptibility to precipitation depends on the type of formulation. Oil-based EC formulations are not weather-sensitive: they bind quickly to the wax layer and are rainproof within an hour. Other contact-acting herbicides have water-based formulations and have to be absorbed via the swollen cuticle, which takes time. Until the absorption process is completed, the herbicide can easily wash off.

Transpiration encourages transport

The water supply to the plant is continuous and involves relatively large quantities of water. This is how the soil-acting herbicide enters the plant via the roots. Absorption depends in turn on the plant's transpiration rate: the more it transpires, the more water (containing herbicide) will flow to the roots. Basically, moist soil and good crop transpiration are important for a herbicide to be effective.

For contact-acting herbicides to be absorbed, it is important that conditions should remain dry for a good six hours after application. During that time the weather should be dull, with a high RH, but dry. Contact-acting herbicides are intended to be absorbed by the leaves of small weeds such as chickweed. Act quickly, because the weeds should not have time to harden off.

Squeezing in a quick spraying with herbicide before it starts to rain is not a clever move. Not only is the drying period probably too short, but drying may also take longer than is stated on the packaging. Before rain, the weather is often cloudy with a high RH, and that is not ideal in terms of drying time.

Herbicide selectivity and weather

The relationship between herbicides after application and the weather conditions depends primarily on the way in which the herbicides work. The selectivity of a bentazone application in peas, for example, is based on a rapid development of the wax layer. After a short spell of high radiation levels, the pea leaves have hardened off to some extent. They can withstand a spraying with bentazone, but many weeds cannot.

Drying time of a crop protection agent

Often, the packaging states how long it needs to stay dry after spraying if a crop protection agent is to work effectively. This is only a very general indication, because drying time depends to a great extent on the weather conditions. If you spray a product such as maneb (a fungicide with a drying time of 6 hours) during sunny weather with an RH of 65 percent, a temperature of 22°C and a wind speed of 4 m/s, it will dry quickly. Within an hour, it has already adhered well to the leaf. On the other hand, if you spray the same product in calm, heavily cloudy weather with an RH of 98 percent and a temperature of 15°C, the stated drying time may be too short. Drying times should therefore be used with caution!

> ### Look out for damage after rain
>
> After a period with a lot of rain, plants are invariably sensitive to a spraying with leaf herbicides. Rain can weaken the protective wax layer in three ways:
>
> - Reduced wax formation.
> - Mechanical damage by raindrops.
> - Damage by splashes of soil. There is a lot of absorption by the swollen cuticle and possibly cracks in the wax due to rapid leaf growth. This can lead to too much crop protection agent being absorbed.

Peas can tolerate spraying with Bentazone well, provided the leaf has hardened off to some extent. A leaf has hardened off once it has experienced a day of dry, sunny weather with a slight breeze.

The active substance is distributed evenly over the leaf after a night with dew. It is important that contact fungicides are applied to the leaf regularly and evenly. Nights with dew contribute towards the ultimate protection.

Fungicides

In the case of fungicides a distinction can be drawn, on the basis of effect, between contact fungicides, systemic fungicides (incl. translaminar) and fungicides with aspects of both. The aim of contact fungicides is to prevent fungal spores from germinating or penetrating the leaf. To this end, the chemical must be distributed evenly over the leaf. Spray the contact fungicide used (maneb, mancozeb) on a dry leaf. In addition, dry and sunny weather is ideal after the application of fungicides of this type because it enables them to dry and adhere quickly. This also works with larger droplets, provided they are distributed evenly over the leaf. In the evening the leaf becomes wet again due to the formation of dew, as a result of which the active substance is redistributed and the protection is maximised.

Rain after spraying

Rain reduces the persistence of contact fungicides, simply because it washes some of the active substance off the plant. Even in the case of frequent sprays with contact fungicides, such as for blight spraying in potatoes or Botrytis spraying in flower bulbs, you should adjust the spraying interval after heavy rain showers.

Contact fungicides should ideally be sprayed during sunny weather with a slight breeze, enabling them to dry quickly on the leaf.

Systemic fungicides

Systemic fungicides (e.g. tebuconazole and prothioconazole) have a completely different mode of transport and activity than contact fungicides. They are absorbed by the leaf and then transported internally in the plant via the vascular system. A germinating fungal is killed as soon as it begins to take nutrients from the plant.

The rate of fungicide transport in the plant depends on the formulation (i.e. the ease with which the crop protection agent dissolves in water) and the systemic properties of the fungicide group. The uptake of systemic fungicides formulated as oil-based ECs is faster than that of fungicides with water-based formulations.

Too much evaporation?

Many farmers believe that too much water and pesticide evaporate if you spray contact fungicides at midday during sunny conditions. But the news here is good! Suppose the spraying rate is 300 litres of water per hectare and the spray nozzles are 50 cm above the crop. The temperature is 23°C and humidity is low, 50 percent. In these conditions, a cubic metre of air holds 20.6 g/m³ x 50 percent = 10.3 grams of moisture. That is 103 litres per hectare in the bottom metre of air. However, spraying takes place at a height of 50 cm, so the true figure is 103 x 0.5 = 51.5 litres per hectare. Even in these extreme conditions, only 17 percent of the spray mixture evaporates. So it is perfectly ok to apply contact fungicides at midday.

Some formulations contain wetting agents, which prevent the crop protection agent from washing off to some extent. In a period of heavy showers or during sprinkle irrigation when there is a chance of products washing off, wetting agents containing latex can also be added (e.g. Bond).

4 Wind, both friend and foe

Wind is air in motion. There is no such thing as a true calm, but the nature of the wind can vary enormously. Wind is of great significance for the agricultural sector, but also one of the least well-understood weather parameters. This is because only the consequences of air movements are visible.

Wind equals transport

The wind ensures the transport of heat and water vapour, both horizontally and vertically. Fungal spores and insects are also spread by the wind. At the same time, wind is vital in protecting plants from diseases and infestations. Natural air displacement helps spray droplets to penetrate the crop.

Drift is also the result of wind. Drift can occur if there is too much wind, but also if there is too little. Everyone is well aware of the risk when there is too much wind, but too little wind is also less than ideal because the wind direction is no longer clear and the drift can move in an unforeseen direction.

Measuring wind

It is difficult to measure wind. It is a swirling air movement, after all. The air moves horizontally and vertically. Speed and direction are important in the case of horizontal movement and both behave capriciously, with several variations per second. The standard height for measuring wind is 10 metres. Wind speed is based on the mean measurement over a ten minute period.

Wind speed indicator

Don't buy a wind speed indicator for your sprayer. There's no point, because wind blows in gusts. To get a reliable indication, you would have to measure continuously for 10 minutes on average. An ordinary wind speed indicator does not record an average speed. In addition, the sprayer disturbs the wind pattern, which always causes the recorded values to be too high. The gustiness of the wind imposes limitations. At a windspeed of 3 m/s gusts regularly reach speeds of 8 to 9 m/s. If it is very turbulent, the wind can easily carry small droplets of pesticide with it to other areas, such as a ditch or a neighbouring crop or field.

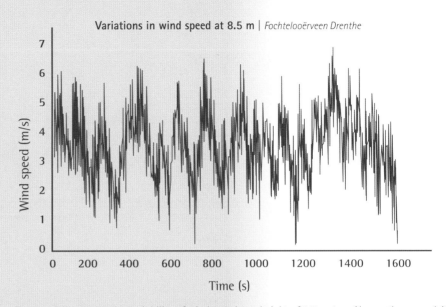

Variations in wind speed at 8.5 m | *Fochtelooërveen Drenthe*

The graph illustrates the variability of wind speed at a height of 8.5 metres. Nearer the ground, it is even more variable.

*W*hen measuring wind, you need to take your time. You can only count on an accurate measurement if you record the mean over 10 minutes.

A turbulent wind can easily carry small droplets of liquid with it to the surface water for example, so always try to spray with the largest possible droplet size.

The wind speed indicator at this weather station is 10 metres above the ground, the standard height for measuring wind speed.

The Beaufort scale

Wind speed is most accurately expressed in metres per second (m/s). This is sometimes converted to km/hour. Weather forecasters may also express wind speed in terms of wind force, usually in units on the Beaufort scale. A near gale, for example, can have a speed of 14 m/s and wind force of 7. In the case of gusts wind speed is particularly important, which is why these are expressed in m/s.

Wind force

The Beaufort scale was originally developed for use at sea and later adopted for use on land. As a result, it is not always easy to interpret. In Beaufort's time wind speed was measured at wave height. When it was adapted to conditions on land, this was converted into fairly subjective concepts such as 'branches broken off trees' or 'slates removed from houses'.

Beaufort scale

Wind force	Description		Wind speed (m/s)
0	Calm	Smoke rises vertically.	0 – 0.3
1	Light air	Direction of wind shown by smoke drift.	0.3 – 1.6
2	Light breeze	Leaves rustle and wind is felt on face.	1.6 – 3.4
3	Gentle breeze	Leaves and small twigs in constant motion; wind extends light flag.	3.4 – 5.5
4	Moderate breeze	Raises dust and loose paper; small branches are moved.	5.5 – 8.0
5	Fresh breeze	Small trees in leaf begin to sway; crested wavelets form on inland waters.	8.0 – 10.8
6	Strong breeze	Large branches in motion; whistling heard in telegraph wires.	10.8 – 13.9
7	Near gale	Whole trees in motion; inconvenience felt when walking against the wind.	13.9 – 17.2
8	Gale	Breaks twigs off trees; generally impedes progress.	17.2 – 20.8
9	Severe gale	Breaks branches off trees. Slight structural damage occurs (chimney-pots and slates removed).	20.8 – 24.5
10	Storm	Trees uprooted; considerable structural damage occurs.	24.5 – 28.5
11	Violent storm	Accompanied by widespread damage.	28.5 – 32.7
12	Hurricane	Nothing left standing.	32.7 and greater

For the average agriculturalist, wind force is not really important. If you are planning to spray, what matters is the wind speed (in m/s) in the layer between the spray nozzle and the plants or soil.

Variable flow

The processes behind air movements are invisible, otherwise you could see that the wind moves in swirls. This is called turbulence. Turbulence is caused by a disturbance of the pattern of the wind. For example, the wind blows against a wheat stalk. The stalk moves with it, but puts up some resistance. The air experiences an inhibiting force and is forced to deviate, triggering the swirl. The causes of turbulence differ widely. In agriculture, two types of turbulent flow are important: boundary layer turbulence and obstacle flow.

Boundary layer turbulence

Wind has a fairly constant speed at higher altitudes (60 metres). At ground level it is curbed (by obstacles like trees and houses) at irregular intervals, resulting in many small swirls which 'pass on' the braking effect upwards. At the bottom the air speed slows down further, occasionally producing a large swirl of air. A large swirl like this is approximately as deep as the bottom layer of air, or 'boundary layer'. The depth of this boundary layer depends to a large extent on the weather conditions and the season. In the growing season a common depth in the daytime is 600 metres.

Smoke drift gives a good indication of boundary layer turbulence. From time to time the smoke meanders downwards sharply, then catches up with an earlier section of the plume from below.

Boundary layer turbulence on arable land

Boundary layer turbulence and convection (rising air) have significant consequences for agriculture. A gust of wind penetrates far into a crop, refreshing the air locally. In the daytime, a good 70 percent of the hourly transpiration takes place in 30 percent of the time! This means extensive mixing of air in the crop. Not only spray mixtures can reach the underside of the leaves, so can fungal spores. Providing a gust of wind does not refresh the air again, the temperature and humidity rise quickly. Transpiration stagnates until a new gust of wind comes along.

The fluctuating speed of the wind is demonstrated by the 'waves' in this plot of wheat.

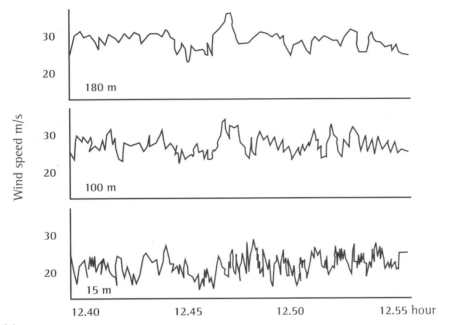

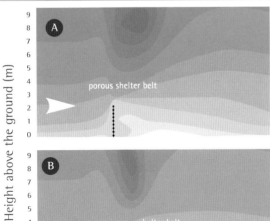

*N*earer the ground, the wind speed drops. The wind 'collides' with obstacles such as trees and buildings. At the same time, the degree of turbulence increases. This is clear from the frequency of wind speed variations.

The figures show that the wind speed decreases behind the shelter belt or spray screen. The turbulent air movements in the shelter belt or spray screen go in the direction of the ground (or the ditch behind). In B the turbulence is much stronger. So work with a spray screen and shelter belts that are sufficiently open and let through a reasonable amount of wind.

Obstacle flow

When the wind meets a solid object, the air is prevented from moving forward. It piles up and the oncoming flow of air is diverted from its course. The wind then goes over and around the obstacle. However, the deviation in wind speed and wind direction begin even before the obstacle. The wind speed drops directly in front of the obstacle. Around it, there is a zone where the wind speed increases, because the oncoming flow of air has to go somewhere. Behind the obstacle is an area of calm. This is an important concept for the agricultural sector, in connection with drift to a ditch or other unintended areas.

Shelter belts are used to check the wind, but turbulence behind the trees can also result in more drift.

No wind? Don't spray!

Arable farmers tend to spray early in the morning, when conditions are calm. My advice is: don't! Whether it is 'spraying weather' depends not only on wind strength, but also on temperature, relative humidity and the likelihood of rain. Too much wind is bad on account of drift. But too little wind (calm) is just as risky. If the sun shines, bubbles of warm air can develop on the surface of the ground. These start to rise (thermals), carrying the crop protection agent with them to places it wasn't meant to go.

Wind is changeable, in both speed and direction. At low wind speeds in particular, the wind direction varies widely. A slightly stronger wind is less easily influenced. It can even be contrary to the prevailing direction at the time of spraying! If you spray in conditions with a slight breeze, you can see where the droplets are blowing. A wind speed of 1–3 m/s at spray nozzle height is ideal.

During air-assisted spraying (left), air is blown downwards at high speed behind the spray nozzle. The flow of air is so powerful that 'horizontal' wind has virtually no effect. In spraying without air assistance (right), a lot of drift is produced.

Spray nozzles do not emit a single droplet size, but a spectrum of small and large droplets all mixed together. The median or mean of this droplet distribution determines the category of the spray nozzle. The number of small droplets increases at higher pressure or with a nozzle with a smaller aperture.

Small drops fall slowly

Small drops with a diameter of 100 μm fall at a rate of around 0.25 m/s. Droplets at a height of fifty centimetres (spray nozzle height) above the crop take two seconds to reach the leaves. In a moderate breeze they can cover 8-10 metres in a gust of wind, so it is better to avoid spraying with small droplets.

A clear example of spray drift because the droplets are too small. The sprayer is probably using a nozzle with a small aperture and too much pressure.

Right droplet size

The choice of a particular droplet size depends on the type of pesticide that you want to spray and the surface on which you are spraying (bare soil or crop). The nozzle size determines the desired droplet size. Take additional precautions if using fine droplets, such as air assistance or a tow sheet. With air-liquid nozzles, droplets prone to drift can be controlled well using a mixture of air and fairly large droplets. This is the case, for example, with venturi nozzles and airtec or airjet nozzles. Another way to limit drift is to spray fine droplets susceptible to drift just above the crop, so that the wind can't get a hold on them. This is the principle on which the Swedish tow sheet (Släpduk) system is based.

Weight and speed of droplets

Larger droplets are heavier and conserve their speed longer. As a result, small droplets are much more susceptible to air movements. This makes them more prone to drift. The sprayer's travelling speed also plays a role. In practice, farmers often notice that going with the wind causes a lot less drift than going against it.

Contact-acting herbicides

In the case of contact-acting herbicides, large drops (>500 μm) hit the cotyledons or leaves of the plant with so much energy that they roll or bounce off. However, less of the herbicide is left behind on the weed (lower retention) and its effectiveness is sometimes reduced as a result. Finer droplets are therefore preferable. The disadvantage is more spray drift.

The relationship between spray nozzle and pressure is a delicate one. For better penetration of the crop you should choose a different nozzle, increase the quantity of spraying water and travel much more slowly. Bear in mind that the water in the spray mixture will ensure transport of the crop protection agent. The photo on the left shows a low-drift venturi nozzle, while the photo on the right is of a non-low-drift standard nozzle.

Because the Släpduk system is suspended closer to the crop and the sheet retains the droplets, it produces very little drift.

Pesticide coverage

During the process of spraying, a pesticide is distributed. This is not the same as, say, spraying a car with paint. In that case, every square millimetre has to be thoroughly coated. All too often, people still claim that you have to spray with fine droplets because good coverage is important. But this is not true for most applications. In recent years a large number of trials have been conducted which show that the effect of larger droplets is sufficient in virtually all cases.

Droplet size of contact fungicides

Spraying a contact fungicide with large droplets has just as much effect as spraying with very fine droplets, provided the distribution on the leaf is good. Dew formation in the evening makes the leaf wet again, re-distributing the active substance.

Droplet size of soil-acting herbicides

After application, soil-acting herbicides are distributed in the soil with the soil moisture. In the case of crops in beds or ridges, it is preferable to spray with a large droplet size. Large droplets are less susceptible to wind. The advantage is better distribution.

Low-drift spray systems:

- Venturi T-jet: drift reduction of up to 75% - 90%
- Air assistance: drift reduction of up to 90 - 95%
- Släpduk system: drift reduction of up to 95% - 98%
- Boom end half-swath nozzle: large reduction next to the last spray nozzle

---

Coarse droplets are less susceptible to wind, which means that the herbicide is distributed properly over both sides of the ridges or beds.

The boom end half-swath nozzle sits next to the last spray nozzle and gives considerable drift reduction.

Droplet size of systemic fungicides

Spraying with coarse droplets is entirely possible with systemic fungicides as well. The active substance enters the leaf after being taken up by the sap flow en route to the leaf or stem tips. The aim here is to maximise absorption into the sap circulation, not crop coverage. A coarser droplet size may also have advantages in terms of drying time in relation to absorption time. Large droplets take up a relatively large surface area. When large droplets dry, the height of the droplet decreases first, then the surface area that it covers. Proportionately, therefore, the surface area through which the fungicide can be absorbed remains larger for longer in comparison with small droplets.

Droplet size of insecticides

Insecticides can also be sprayed with larger droplets. Insects are often mobile and encounter the insecticides themselves by coming into contact with them or eating parts of the plant that have been sprayed. Some insecticides such as primicarb also have a vapour phase effect, wich may improve insecticidal activity. Only when spraying with synthetic pyrethroids is a slightly finer droplet necessary. Synthetic pyrethroids are not systemic and do not re-distribute themselves.

Droplet size of fungicides in onions

In onions, it is difficult to achieve good retention of fungicides for the control of downy mildew and leaf blight. The upright leaf position and the shape of the leaf are not conducive to good adhesion of the fungicide. When spraying fungicides in onions, therefore, use fine droplets in order to maximise their retention. The use of a spreading product will also improve adhesion and spreading.

The coarser spray droplets of this low-drift spray nozzle are clearly visible. Drift is virtually eliminated.

Legislation

In many countries, the maximum wind speed at which spraying is permitted is set at 5 m/s at 50 cm above the soil or crop. You often hear that this level is reached at a wind speed of 3 on the Beaufort scale. But take care: wind speed has to be measured 50 cm above the soil or crop. The wind speed (in Beaufort units) is measured at a height of 10 metres. Converted to the Beaufort scale, a wind speed of 5 m/s equates to a wind force of 5 to 6 Beaufort units in open areas and areas with fairly large height differences, up to wind force 6 to 7 in more forested areas. At such high wind speeds, sensible farmers have long since stopped spraying.

Changing wind strength

The wind strength changes over the course of the day. Mornings are often fairly calm but the wind can pick up as the day progresses. The wind is strongest in the middle of the afternoon, around three o'clock. After that, it declines in force again. Wind direction is also not constant throughout the day. As the wind picks up over the course of the day, it blows clockwise. Towards the end of the day it dies down a little, and now blows anticlockwise. When the sun goes down, this process stops very quickly and the wind near ground level drops.

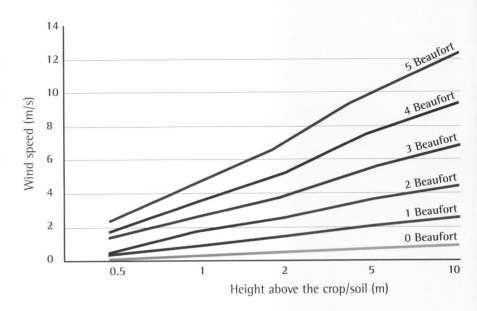

The graph shows clearly that a wind speed of 5 m/s at a height of 50 cm is not yet reached at a wind force of 6 on the Beaufort scale.

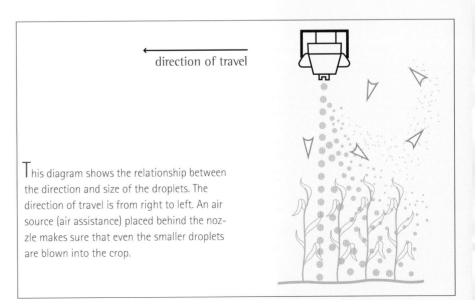

This diagram shows the relationship between the direction and size of the droplets. The direction of travel is from right to left. An air source (air assistance) placed behind the nozzle makes sure that even the smaller droplets are blown into the crop.

5 Resources
and information

The relationship between weather and crop protection is a complicated one. Spraying means taking a range of factors into account: how is the pesticide formulated, where does it work in or on the plant, what were the weather conditions in the last few hours or days and what does the weather forecast say? A number of resources and additional information sources can help you answer these questions.

Decision support systems

Decision support systems (DSS) have been developed to assist farmers. These systems are supplied with meteorological information, which you can also measure yourself. Together with a range of other resources such as fax services, decision support systems form an important link in the chain of integrated agriculture. And where specific information is still lacking, there is always your agricultural extension officer or advisor.

Decision support systems rely on both current and historical meteorological data and weather forecasts. This information is generally obtained from the national weather institutes, possibly supplemented by regional/local weather stations.

Don't rely on them blindly

Decision support systems merely assist farmers in deciding whether or not to treat crops and should not be used prescriptively. However, the use of such systems does appear to reduce the chance of crop damage due to pests and diseases. Reducing the cost of crop protection and minimising the pesticide burden on the environment are other advantages. Working with decision support systems enables you to choose the optimum time for pesticide treatment, and often makes it possible to reduce the application rate without an increase in the risk of resistance.

Potato late blight

Late blight of potatoes, caused by the pathogen *Phytophthora infestans*, can cause enormous damage resulting in loss of tuber yield and quality. In blight favourable weather, farmers may treat potatoes with fungicides every five to seven days during the growing season. In this case, favourable weather means frequent rainfall and/or a long leaf wetness duration at temperatures between 12 and 24°C. Using a decision support system based on these parameters and an appreciation of blight activity in the locality together with crop development, spray intervals can be adjusted and shortened in times when there is a high risk of infection. Examples of decision support systems for potato late blight include Blightwatch.co.uk, which uses Smith Periods, provided by the UK Met Office. Another system is Forecast Xtra, based on the Dutch Plant-Plus

Set up temperature and relative humidity sensors in the right place, otherwise the data will be misinterpreted in the decision support system.

model, where the weather data are supplied by small local weather stations. In the case of Blightwatch/Smith Periods the advice service covers the whole of the UK, while the advice provided by Forecast-Xtra can be tailored to farm-specific conditions.

Periods with a high risk of late blight in potatoes can generally be predicted reliably with the aid of decision support systems.

Fire (Botrytis) causes brown, necrotic patches on leaves and stems. Common forms are Botrytis tulipae in tulips, Botrytis elliptica in lilies and Botrytis gladiolorum in gladioli. This is B. elliptica.

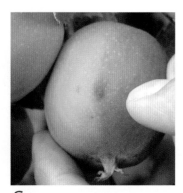

Scab can infect both leaves and fruit in apples (Venturia inaequalis) and pears (Venturia pirina). The infection takes the form of brown and grey patches.

Pest and diseases in vegetables

Plant-Plus and the Morph/HRI group in Warwick, England have developed a number of pest and disease models for cabbage and root vegetables.

Morph-group

The Morph/HRI group MORPH (which stands for Methods Of Research Practice in Horticulture) is a software framework containing computer models. These models use weather in various ways. Some combine the regional data collected during the current season with forecasts for the next few weeks, while others use local, intensively collected data to give a precise indication of events during the last few days.

The results of Morph models can take the form of tables, spreadsheets or graphs for interpretation by growers and consultant agronomists. The models can be divided into three groups: Top Fruit models (apple scab, powdery mildew, Nectria fruit rot, fireblight, codling moth, tortrix moth and pear psyllid), vegetable/cabbage diseases (Alternaria, ring spot and white blister) and vegetable/cabbage pests (cabbage root fly, carrot fly, pollen beetle and narcissus fly).

Another commercial provider of pest/disease warnings is Plant-Plus from the Netherlands. Using official meteorological data, their models give advice on various vegetable pests such as onion downy mildew, onion Botrytis, leek white tip, leek rust, carrot Alternaria, carrot Scle-rotinia, brassica ringspot, Alternaria in brassicas, white blister in cabbage, lettuce mildew and celery leaf blight. Plant-Plus also advises on carrot fly and leek thrips.

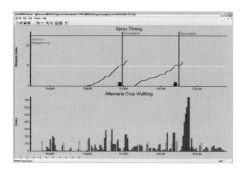

Example of a decision support system advising on leaf spots in cabbage. The image shows the disease index and then advises when to apply fungicides.

Scab in apples and pears

Scab is the main fungal disease affecting quality in apples and pears. Decision support systems can indicate clearly when the scab ascospores are released, for example, and give advance warning of weather that brings a high risk of infection, and which pesticide is best to use. Four systems are in use in the UK: Ventem, Adem, the Welte model and the RIMpro model.

GEWIS

Decision support systems are of little value if the spraying conditions are unfavourable and the active substance cannot be absorbed or transported to where it is meant to work. A unique decision support system is GEWIS, a Dutch abbreviation standing for 'crop protection and weather information system'. This system integrates all of the available information on the different types of crop protection agents (insecticides, growth regulators, fungicides, herbicides, chemical defoliation agents, etc.) in relation to weather conditions. It models all of the processes of uptake, transport and mode of activity of the various crop protection agents. While the individual decision support systems advise on spraying, which pesticide to use and/or which application rate, GEWIS identifies the time when the recommended spray treatment will have the maximum effect.

Lower application rate required

If GEWIS indicates that a spraying is likely to be highly effective, you can often reduce the application rate of the pesticide without the risk of resistance developing. Following the advice as to the best time of application in the day can make a difference in terms of the costs of contact-acting herbicides, growth regulators and insecticides.

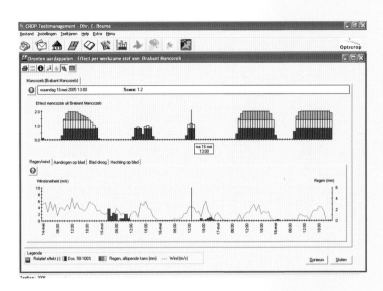

The graph shows the effectiveness of a spraying hour by hour. Each bar represents a different hour of the day. The system is very user-friendly.

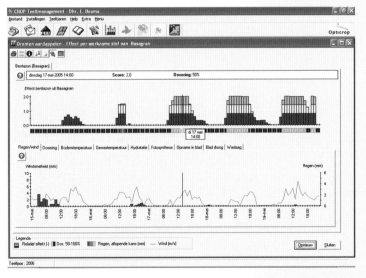

If you spray during a period of high effectiveness, you can reduce the application rate. The graph shows that the application rate in this case can be reduced by as much as 50 percent (under the blue blocks).

Wireless, automatic weather stations are used to measure weather data in the field.

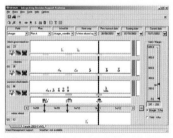

Advice on applying herbicides after consultation of DESSAC. This decision support system can also be accessed via special Internet sites.

Leaf blight and downy mildew

Two fungal diseases cause serious damage and loss of yield in onions: leaf blight (*Botrytis squamosa*) and downy mildew (*Peronospora destructor*). Like most fungi, leaf blight thrives in warm, moist weather. Downy mildew can spread rapidly and, depending on the temperature and leaf wetness durations, 80 percent of the crop can succumb to downy mildew in as little as 14 days. To control both diseases, two decision support systems have been developed. Usually applied in combination, they are Botcast/SIV and Downcast.

DESSAC

DESSAC (Decision Support Systems for Arable Crops) is a decision support system which provides its users with information and assistance in exploring the decisions available, but does not take the decision or the responsibility for that decision away from the user. DESSAC is a combination of several databases (including data on weather, varieties, fertilisers and pesticides) and four modules of decision support systems: the wheat disease manager, a system for decision support for oilseed rape pests, a system for weed management and a model for the simulation of nitrogen in arable land.

Agricultural information

In the UK, the Met Office and BBC Weather use a number of maps of the United Kingdom to show the weather situation with respect to general meteorological factors, but do not provide specific agricultural weather reports.

In Ireland, the Irish Meteorological Service provides specific weather reports for farmers online. It also warns about the spread of potato blight from May to September, forest fire risk, frost for top fruit growers in spring and advises the Department of Agriculture on the risk and prevalence of animal diseases, e.g. airborne spread of foot and mouth disease virus.

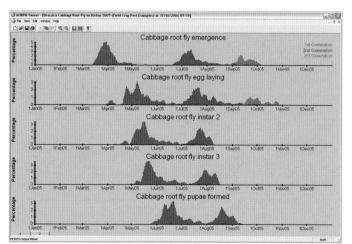

With the help of graphs the development of the different generations of the cabbage root fly can be made visible. Control measurements can be taken at the right moment.

Online info

Information on the relationship between weather and plant diseases is available daily online from a number of agrochemical manufacturers such as Syngenta. Syngenta provides an SMS service for warnings relating to Alternaria, white blister and ringspot in brassicas.

DIY measuring

You can easily measure many weather parameters yourself. Measure temperature and humidity in a Stevenson's screen if possible. These allow wind to pass through freely but keep out sun and rain. The screen walls are white-painted strips of wood in the form of a venetian blind to keep out direct sunlight.

Temperature

Temperature can be measured reliably using a digital thermometer.

Humidity

Humidity can be measured with a hygrometer. This could be a hair hygrometer or a digital version. Provided they are kept clean, both sensors can be very accurate.

Grass minimum temperature

On clear nights the air just above the surface of the ground cools down most. This is where to install a grass minimum thermometer, a thermometer which is set up at a height of exactly 10 cm over short-mown grass under a white covering plate.

A Stevenson's screen allows wind to pass through but is impervious to sun and rain.

A Stevenson's screen can be used to measure a number of weather parameters. It can be important not only for recording weather but may help explain good or poor spraying results.

Precipitation

Simple rain gauges made of glass or plastic are hard to read, and break easily in the event of frost. A better option is a Hellman rain gauge with a collection area of 200 or 400 cm². This rain gauge has a sharp edge to define the collection area precisely. The water runs into an internal reservoir via a narrow funnel.

Wind direction and speed

It's often difficult setting up a wind direction and wind speed meter (anemometer) at a height of 10 metres in the open fields, which is why they are usually installed on a roof. The values obtained are generally reliable, provided you take account of disturbances due to obstacles such as nearby trees or houses.

Measuring air pressure

Air pressure is measured using a barometer. Changes in air pressure over a given period can give an indication of imminent changes in the weather. Generally speaking, there are two different types of barometer: the liquid barometer and the metal or aneroid barometer.

A liquid barometer consists of a U-shaped tube which is sealed at one end. The sealed end is not affected by air pressure, unlike the other end. The liquid in the tube should be at the same level if the pressure is the same at both ends. This enables you to measure the air pressure. A metal barometer consists of a small metal box. When the air pressure rises, the top of the box is pushed downwards.

The box contains a spring that keeps the top of the box in the same position. The forces acting on the spring can be measured. Metal barometers are less sensitive to temperature than liquid barometers but, when connected to a digital counter, they have the advantage of being relatively easy to read.

*M*ini electronic weather stations give a reasonably reliable and straightforward picture of forthcoming changes in the weather. They may represent changes in air pressure in the form of a graph, for example.

A Hellman rain gauge can be used to measure precipitation accurately without losing too much moisture to wind effects and evaporation.

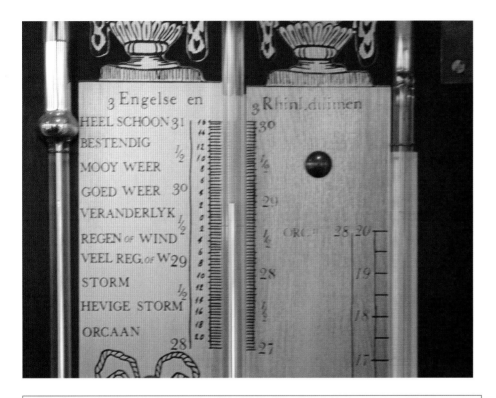

A mercury barometer records changes in air pressure very accurately. Such changes may herald the approach of a turn in the weather.

In the days before there were accurate instruments for measuring changes in air pressure, the thunder glass or storm glass was very popular. When the pressure fell, the water level in the spout rose. Bad weather was on the way!

Weather stations

Surprisingly accurate, mini weather stations are commercially available nowadays (see table), but do bear in mind the price/quality ratio.

Brand	Usefulness in the agricultural sector	Can it be connected to a PC?
BAR, various models	Limited, measure current data	No
Cresta, various models	Limited, measure current data	No
La Crosse, various models	Limited, measure current data	No
TFA, various WS models	Limited, measure current data	Yes, the more expensive types
Oregon scientific/ Huger, various models	Limited, clear presentation of weather changes	Yes, the more expensive types
Davis Vantage Pro2	Clearly useful	Yes

Consider first of all how you plan to use the data from your weather station. Do you need a PC connection or can you manage without? Most mini electronic weather stations are fairly accurate, but don't forget to clean the sensors regularly!

6 Practical applications

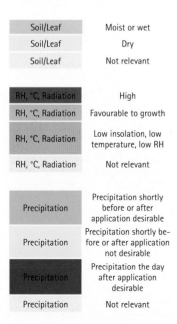

LEGEND

Soil/Leaf	Moist or wet
Soil/Leaf	Dry
Soil/Leaf	Not relevant

RH, °C, Radiation	High
RH, °C, Radiation	Favourable to growth
RH, °C, Radiation	Low insolation, low temperature, low RH
RH, °C, Radiation	Not relevant

Precipitation	Precipitation shortly before or after application desirable
Precipitation	Precipitation shortly before or after application not desirable
Precipitation	Precipitation the day after application desirable
Precipitation	Not relevant

Cereals

Soil-acting herbicides (p. 50)

True soil-acting herbicides are usually applied in the autumn after sowing. Take care: the ideal weather conditions to obtain the best possible effect of the herbicide are different before and after application!

Before application, herbicides need the following conditions in order to be effective:

Soil	Leaf	RH	°C	Radiation	Precipitation

After application they need the following weather conditions:

Soil	Leaf	RH	°C	Radiation	Precipitation

True soil-acting herbicides include isoproturon, pendimethalin, diflufencan/isoproturon, prosulfocarb and bifenox/isoproturon.

Soil-acting herbicides with contact-acting effect (p. 50)

The ideal conditions for these soil-acting herbicides are slightly different due to the additional contact-acting effect on the leaf.
Ideal conditions for application:

Soil	Leaf	RH	°C	Radiation	Precipitation

Soil-acting herbicides with contact-acting effect include bromoxynil/diflufenican/ioxynil and prosulfocarb.

Contact-acting herbicides (p. 35)

Contact-acting herbicides come in two groups: the ALS inhibitors group and the PPO inhibitors group.

ALS inhibitors group

Night frosts around the time of application of products in this group are extremely undesirable!
Ideal conditions for application:

Soil	Leaf	RH	°C	Radiation	Precipitation

Contact-acting herbicides in the ALS inhibitors group include metsulfuron-methyl, iodosulfuron-methyl-sodium, florasulam and florasulam/fluroxypyr.

PPO inhibitors group

Ideal conditions for application:

Soil	Leaf	RH	°C	Radiation	Precipitation

Contact-acting herbicides in the PPO inhibitors group include cafentrazone-ethyl.

Hormone herbicides and ACCase inhibitors (p. 35)

Ideal conditions for application:

| Soil | Leaf | RH | °C | Radiation | Precipitation |

The hormone herbicides: fluroxypyr and ACCase inhibitors: fenoxaprop-P-ethyl.

Growth regulators (see also p. 35)

Ideal conditions for application:

| Soil | Leaf | RH | °C | Radiation | Precipitation |

Growth regulator: trinexapac-ethyl.

Cereal fungicides (p. 15 and 39)

Fungicides can be divided into three groups: triazoles, morpholines and strobilurins.

Triazoles

Ideal conditions for application:

| Soil | Leaf | RH | °C | Radiation | Precipitation |

Fungicides in the triazoles group include cyproconazole/propiconazole, cyproconazole, triadimenol/tebuconazole, epoxyconazole/fenpropimorph and propiconazole.

Morpholines

Ideal conditions for application:

| Soil | Leaf | RH | °C | Radiation | Precipitation |

Fungicides in the morpholines group are fenpropimorf and fenpropidin, quinoxyfen, proquinazid, cyflufenamid and metrafenone.

Strobilurins (p. 39)

Ideal conditions for application:

| Soil | Leaf | RH | °C | Radiation | Precipitation |

Fungicides in the strobilurins group include picoxystrobin, kresoxim-methyl/epoxiconazol, azoxystrobin, azoxistrobin/chlorothalonil, pyraclostrobine/epoxiconazole, trifloxystrobin/cyproconazole and trifloxystrobin.

Other leaf and ear fungicides (p. 39)

Ideal conditions for application:

| Soil | Leaf | RH | °C | Radiation | Precipitation |

Fungicides in this group include chlorothalonil and mancozeb.

LEGEND

Soil/Leaf	Moist or wet
Soil/Leaf	Dry
Soil/Leaf	Not relevant

RH, °C, Radiation	High
RH, °C, Radiation	Favourable to growth
RH, °C, Radiation	Low insolation, low temperature, low RH
RH, °C, Radiation	Not relevant

Precipitation	Precipitation shortly before or after application desirable
Precipitation	Precipitation shortly before or after application not desirable
Precipitation	Precipitation the day after application desirable
Precipitation	Not relevant

(cereals, continued)

Insecticides (see also p. 14 and 15)

As far as the ideal weather conditions for insecticides are concerned, there is a difference between non-pyrethroids and pyrethroids.

Non-pyrethroids

Ideal conditions for application:

Cereal insecticides (non-pyrethroids) include pirimicarb and dimethoate.

Pyrethroids

Ideal conditions for application:

Cereal insecticides (pyrethroids) include deltamethrin, lambda-cyhalothrin and esfenvalerate.

Sugarbeet

Soil-acting herbicides (p. 50)

True soil-acting herbicides are applied shortly after sowing. The ideal weather conditions before and after sowing are different.
Before application, the following conditions are needed:

After application the ideal conditions are as follows:

Soil-acting herbicides include ethofumesate.

Contact-acting herbicides (p. 35)

Frequent sunshine in the days immediately after application improves the effect of contact-acting herbicides.
Ideal conditions for application:

Contact-acting herbicides include phenmedipham and desmedipham, clopyralid.

Volunteer potato control herbicides (p. 35)

Ideal conditions for application:

Two agents for the control of volunteer potatoes are glyphosate and clopyralid.

ACCase inhibitors (p. 70)

Ideal conditions for application:

ACCase inhibitors include quizalofop-P-ethyl, cycloxidim, fluazifop-P-butyl and tepraloxydim.

Insecticides (p. 14 and 15)

As far as the ideal conditions for the effect of insecticides are concerned, there is a difference between non-pyrethroids and pyrethroids.

Non-pyrethroids

Ideal conditions for application:

Insecticides (non-pyrethroids) include pirimicarb, dimethoate and triazamate.

Pyrethroids

Ideal conditions for application:

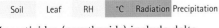

Insecticides (pyrethroids) include deltamethrin and lambda-cyhalothrin.

Fungicides

Ideal conditions for application:

Fungicides permitted in beets

Fungicides permitted in beets include triazoles (e.g. difenoconazole), strobilurins (e.g. pyraclostrobin), morpholines (e.g. fenpropidin, quinoxyfen and sulphur).

LEGEND

Soil/Leaf	Moist or wet
Soil/Leaf	Dry
Soil/Leaf	Not relevant

RH, °C, Radiation	High
RH, °C, Radiation	Favourable to growth
RH, °C, Radiation	Low insolation, low temperature, low RH
RH, °C, Radiation	Not relevant

Precipitation	Precipitation shortly before or after application desirable
Precipitation	Precipitation shortly before or after application not desirable
Precipitation	Precipitation the day after application desirable
Precipitation	Not relevant

Onions

Soil-acting herbicides (p. 50)

When applying true soil-acting herbicides after sowing, it is important that the soil should not be too coarse. The ideal conditions before and after application are different.

Before application, the following weather conditions are needed:

| Soil | Leaf | RH | °C | Radiation | Precipitation |

After application the weather conditions should be as follows:

| Soil | Leaf | RH | °C | Radiation | Precipitation |

A soil herbicide used in onions is pendimethalin.

Soil-acting herbicides with contact-acting effect

The best conditions for soil-acting herbicides with a contact-acting effect, which are usually applied after sowing, are as follows:

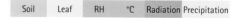

| Soil | Leaf | RH | °C | Radiation | Precipitation |

Soil-acting herbicides with a contact-acting effect include chlorpropham or chloridazon/chlorpropham.

Contact-acting herbicides
(p. 35 and 50)

At the flag stage and in onion shoots longer than 3 cm (the stage of development is important!) contact-acting herbicides can be applied to control small weeds. Many of these herbicides are in fact harmful to the onions. Use large droplets to minimise retention (adhesion) on the crop and to ensure that as much of the herbicide as possible runs off the leaf. Don't spray too soon after a spell of dull, good growing weather, and wait until the onions have hardened off a little.
Ideal conditions for application:

| Soil | Leaf | RH | °C | Radiation | Precipitation |

Contact-acting herbicides include chloorpropham, chloridazon/chlorpropham or pendimethalin + chlorpropham.

Application of MH
(maleic hydrazide) (p. 35)

To ensure good absorption and later effect of MH, good growing weather is needed both before and after application, with average daytime temperatures of 15°C and no excessively sunny periods. The leaf should remain moist as long as possible after spraying, to maximise the absorption period. Rain within 5 hours or so after application is not good because it will wash off much of the active substance.
Ideal conditions for application:

| Soil | Leaf | RH | °C | Radiation | Precipitation |

Fungicides (p. 39 and 62)

Fungicides can be divided into three groups: systemic fungicides, strobilurins and contact-acting fungicides.

Systemic fungicides

Ideal conditions for application:

| Soil | Leaf | RH | °C | Radiation | Precipitation |

Systemic fungicide includes chlorothalonil/metalaxyl-M.

Strobilurins (p. 39 and 62)

| Soil | Leaf | RH | °C | Radiation | Precipitation |

Fungicides in the strobilurin group includes azoxystrobin.

Contact-acting fungicides (p. 39 and 62)

Ideal conditions for application:

| Soil | Leaf | RH | °C | Radiation | Precipitation |

Contact-acting fungicides include chlorothalonil and iprodion.

Insecticides (p. 14 and 15)

As far as the ideal conditions for the effect of insecticides are concerned, there is a difference between non-pyrethroids and pyrethroids.

Non-pyrethroids

Ideal conditions for application:

| Soil | Leaf | RH | °C | Radiation | Precipitation |

Two insecticides in this category (non-pyrethroid) are chlorpyrifos or spinosad.

LEGEND

Swatch	Meaning
Soil/Leaf	Moist or wet
Soil/Leaf	Dry
Soil/Leaf	Not relevant
RH, °C, Radiation	High
RH, °C, Radiation	Favourable to growth
RH, °C, Radiation	Low insolation, low temperature, low RH
RH, °C, Radiation	Not relevant
Precipitation	Precipitation shortly before or after application desirable
Precipitation	Precipitation shortly before or after application not desirable
Precipitation	Precipitation the day after application desirable
Precipitation	Not relevant

Potatoes

Soil-acting herbicides (p. 50)

True soil-acting herbicides are usually applied in the spring after setting. The ideal conditions for maximum effect are different before and after application.
Before application the following conditions are needed:

After application the ideal weather conditions are as follows:

Soil-acting herbicides include linuron, prosulfocarb, metribuzin, clomazone and flufenacet.

Soil-acting herbicides with contact-acting effect (p. 50)

The ideal conditions for these soil-acting herbicides are slightly different because they also have a contact-acting effect on the leaf.
Ideal conditions for application:

Soil-acting herbicides with a contact-acting effect include metribuzin and prosulfocarb.

Contact-acting herbicides (p. 35)

Contact-acting herbicides can be divided into two groups: the ALS inhibitors group and the PPO-inhibitors group.

ALS inhibitors group

Night frosts around the time of spraying are extremely undesirable for this group! Ideal conditions for application:

The ALS inhibitors group includes rimsulfuron.

PPO inhibitors group

The application of products in the PPO-inhibitors group requires the following weather conditions:

The PPO-inhibitors group includes bentazone and metribuzin.

Defoliation (p. 35)

Defoliation products or dessicants are used to aid the harvesting of potato crops and can be divided into two groups: diquat and the PPO inhibitors, and the phosphonic acids.

Diquat and the PPO inhibitors

Ideal conditions for application:

Diquat-like agents include diquat and carfentrazone-ethyl + oil.

Phosphonic acids

Ideal conditions for application:

Metoxuron-like agents include glufosinate-ammonium.

ACCase inhibitors (p. 35)

Ideal conditions for application:

The growth substance and grass herbicide group includes cycloxydim.

Fungicides for the control of Phytophthora (p. 39)

Ideal conditions for application:

This group includes chlorothalonil, mancozeb, cyazofamid, fluazinam, mancozeb/dimethomorph, mancozeb/cymoxanil, famoxate/cymoxanil, mancozeb/mefenoxam, chlorothalonil/propamocarb-hydrochloride, mancozeb/benthiavalicarb-isopropyl and mefenoxam/fluazinam.

Insecticides (p. 14 and 15)

As far as the ideal conditions for the application of insecticides are concerned, there is a difference between non-pyrethroids and pyrethroids.

Non-pyrethroids

Ideal conditions for application:

Potato insecticides (non-pyrethroids) include pirimicarb and pymetrozine.

(potatoes, continued)

Pyrethroids
Ideal conditions for application:

Soil	Leaf	RH	°C	Radiation	Precipitation

Potato insecticides (pyrethroids) include lambda-cyhalothrin.

Insecticides for the control of virus transmission in seed potatoes (p. 14 and 15)

Soil	Leaf	RH	°C	Radiation	Precipitation

Oilseed Rape

Soil-acting herbicides (p. 50)

Soil-acting herbicides are usually applied in the spring after planting. The ideal conditions before and after application are different.
Before application, the following conditions are needed:

Soil	Leaf	RH	°C	Radiation	Precipitation

After application, the following weather conditions are needed:

Soil	Leaf	RH	°C	Radiation	Precipitation

Soil-acting herbicides include metazachlor, metazachlor/quinmerac, clomazone, napropamid, propyzamide and trifluralin.

LEGEND

Soil/Leaf	Moist or wet
Soil/Leaf	Dry
Soil/Leaf	Not relevant

RH, °C, Radiation	High
RH, °C, Radiation	Favourable to growth
RH, °C, Radiation	Low insolation, low temperature, low RH
RH, °C, Radiation	Not relevant

Precipitation	Precipitation shortly before or after application desirable
Precipitation	Precipitation shortly before or after application not desirable
Precipitation	Precipitation the day after application desirable
Precipitation	Not relevant

Cereal and ACCase inhibitors (p. 35)

Ideal conditions for application:

The cereal and ACCase inhibitors include tepraloxydim, cycloxydim, fluazifop-P-butyl and quizalofop-P-ethyl.

Growth regulators (see also p. 35)

The ideal weather conditions for application are:

Growth regulators include metconazole and tebuconazole.

Oilseed rape fungicides

Fungicides can be divided into three groups: systemic fungicides and strobilurins (or strobilurin-like fungicides) which are somewhere between systemic and non-systemic.

Systemic fungicides

The ideal weather conditions for application are:

Systemic fungicides include metconazole, difenoconazole, tebuconazole, carbendazim/flusilazole, prochloraz and prothioconazole.

Strobilurins (strobilurin-like fungicides) (see also p. 37)

The ideal weather conditions for application are:

Fungicides in the strobilurin group or products that work well under the same weather conditions include boscalid.

Insecticides (see also pp. 14 and 15)

Pyrethroids

The ideal weather conditions during and after application are:

Oilseed rape insecticides (pyrethroids) include beta-cyfluthrin, deltamethrin, alphacypermethrin, zetacypermethrin and lambda-cyhalothrin.

LEGEND

Soil/Leaf	Moist or wet
Soil/Leaf	Dry
Soil/Leaf	Not relevant

RH, °C, Radiation	High
RH, °C, Radiation	Favourable to growth
RH, °C, Radiation	Low insolation, low temperature, low RH
RH, °C, Radiation	Not relevant

Precipitation	Precipitation shortly before or after application desirable
Precipitation	Precipitation shortly before or after application not desirable
Precipitation	Precipitation the day after application desirable
Precipitation	Not relevant

Maize

Soil-acting herbicides (p. 50)

Soil-acting herbicides are applied after sowing. The ideal weather conditions before and after application are different. Before application, the following conditions are required:

After application, the weather conditions required are as follows:

Soil-acting herbicides include pendimethalin.

Soil-acting herbicides with contact-acting effect (p. 50)

The ideal conditions for these soil-acting herbicides are slightly different because they also have a contact-acting effect on the leaf.
Ideal conditions for application:

Soil-acting herbicides with contact-acting effect include mesotrione.

Contact-acting herbicides (p. 35)

Contact-acting herbicides can be divided into two groups: the ALS inhibitors group and the Others group.

ALS inhibitors group

Night frosts around the time of application of these agents are extremely undesirable!
Ideal conditions for application:

The ALS inhibitors group includes rimsulfuron and nicosulfuron.

Other contact herbicide group

Ideal conditions for application:

This group includes bromoxynil, pyridate and terbuthylazine.

Volunteer potato and couch grass control (p. 35)

Ideal conditions for application:

One agent used is glyphosate.

Bindweed control (p. 35)

Ideal conditions for application:

Agents include fluroxypyr.

Index

Roodbont agricultural public⁙⁙ns

In addition to Weather & Crop Protection Roodbont offers many other practical and user-friendly books about various aspects of agriculture. Our books are available in various languages. You can order them directly from our website (www.roodbont.nl), by telephone (+31 575 54 56 88) or by email (info@roodbont.nl). There is a charge (minimum € 5.00) for orders from abroad, to cover postage and packing.

Signals series

Cow Signals®

Cow Signals® presents highly practical, reader-friendly information on animal-oriented cattle farming via books, posters, workshops, talks and customised courses. For more details on workshops and courses:
www.vetvice.nl. Tel.: (+31) 165 30 43 05, email: info@vetvice.nl.

Cow Signals

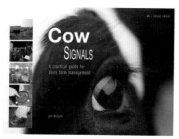

A practical guide for dairy farm management, 96 pages, page size 16.8 x 23.5 cm (landscape), € 25.90, £17.90.
ISBN 978-90-75280-65-4

Co⁙

Hooves

A practical guide for hoof health, 40 pages, page size 16.8 x 23.5 cm (landscape), €15.90, £10.90. ISBN 978-90-75280-00-5

From calf to heifer

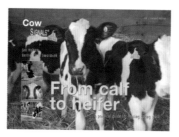

A practical guide for rearing young stock, 40 pages, page size 16.8 x 23.5 cm (landscape), € 15.90, £10.90. ISBN 978-90-75280-95-1

Pig Signals®

Pig Signals® presents highly practical, reader-friendly information on animal-oriented pig farming via books, posters, workshops, talks and customised courses. For more details on workshops and courses: www.3drie3.nl.
Tel.: (+31) 499 31 01 42,
email: kscheepens@vetvice.com

Pig Signals

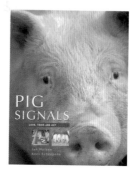

Look, think, act, 96 pages, page size 20.4 x 26.5 cm (landscape,) € 29.90, £20.90. ISBN 978-90-75280-77-7

Crafty Crosses

More information on these and many other books on our website: www.roodbont.nl

ROODBONT
PUBLISHERS